FOR

EYES ONLY!

THE QUAHOG Informant

OCAL LAD'S

OUD

MENT!!!!!

CONTENTS

Published 2012
Pedigree Books Limited, Beech Hill House, Walnut Gardens, Exeter, Devon EX4 4DH
www.pedigreebooks.com | books@pedigreegroup.co.uk

Pedigree®

£7.99

THE QUAHOG INFORMANT

MEET THE

WELCOME TO QUAHOG, RHODE ISLAND, HOME OF THE GRIFFIN CLAN, A FAMILY WHO CAN'T HELP GETTING INTO A NEVER-ENDING SERIES OF CRAZY ADVENTURES, RANGING FROM TIME TRAVEL TO GETTING SENT TO PRISON.

Peter Griffin

"I SAW SOMETHING ON TV I WANNA IMITATE!"

From his earliest days, Peter Löwenbräu Griffin hasn't had a normal life. Raised the son of a strict Catholic, it was only after his dad Francis died that he discovered his real father was a drunken Irishman called Mickey McFinnigan, who his mother Thelma had a brief fling with. Even his birth was unusual as he was born in Mexico after Thelma went there for an abortion.

Officially Peter is mentally retarded but still managed to marry the beautiful Lois and become the father of three, loving his two sons and begrudgingly accepting having Meg for a daughter. When we first met him he worked at a toy factory, later becoming a fisherman, and ultimately getting a job in the shipping department of the Pawtucket Patriot brewery. It may be an everyday job, but Peter's days are filled with all manner of madness, ranging from an ongoing feud with a giant chicken to briefly becoming the President of his own country!

Lois Griffin

"WHAT WAS THAT? WHAT IS SHE, YOUR GRANDMOTHER? THAT'S NO KISS, WATCH THIS!"

The Griffin matriarch comes from a privileged background as she's the daughter of the fabulously wealthy Carter and Barbara Pewterschmidt. However from an early age she had a bit of a rebellious streak, starring in an adult movie and being so promiscuous that in her youth she was known as 'Loose Lois'.

After meeting Peter at her Aunt Marguerite's house (where Peter was working as a towel boy), the two began dating and soon fell in love. While Carter tried to destroy the romance – even trying to kill Peter – he failed and the two married. Lois now likes to present an upright façade, but behind that she has a wicked streak, becoming a kleptomaniac, occasionally revealing a sadomasochistic streak and generally taking things to the extreme. Despite the fact she's approaching middle age, Lois is still a good-looking woman, able to get the likes of Quagmire and Brian in a fervour over her attractiveness.

Meg Griffin

"I LIKE HIM, HE REMEMBERS MY NAME"

It's a big year for Meg as she's going to turn 18, but that doesn't mean her life's going to be easy. The perpetually beanie hatted one goes through life being hated and put down by virtually everyone around her. She has only a few incredibly nerdy friends and her attempts to be more popular nearly always end in failure. Whether it's pretending to be a lesbian, accidentally joining a suicide cult or causing a boy to shoot his brother just so he doesn't have to go on a date with her, Meg's efforts to be accepted are generally disastrous.

Although her parents occasionally say kind things to her, most of the time it's a series of insults and

GRIFFINS!

THIS YEAR THEIR ESCAPADES HAVE BEEN JUST AS NUTS AS EVER, SO JOIN US AS WE HAVE SOME FUN WITH THE GRIFFINS. BUT WHO IS THIS CRAZY FAMILY? WELL, MEET THE GRIFFINS...

unpleasantness. For the eldest child of the Griffin family it's just a case of trying to get through school and hope that life on the other side is more pleasant.

Chris Griffin

"OH NO! SOMEONE PEED IN MY PANTS!"

Christopher Cross Griffin is a bit like his dad, as he's not exactly the smartest of children and he could do with losing a bit of weight. Now in his mid-teens, he's probably the most normal of the Griffin children, even if he is incredibly dim. His stupidity may well be Lois' fault, who's admitted that she smoke and drank a lot while pregnant with him, in the hopes of inducing a miscarriage. Despite his lack of smarts he has shown some talent, briefly becoming a famous artist in New York.

Chris has had his fair share of problems, such as the evil monkey who lived in his closet. While it took years to convince anyone the monkey was real, it turns out Chris had misjudged his nemesis, as the simian was merely misunderstood. The teenager also technically has a wife in the South American jungle, who he inadvertently got hitched to when he ran away to join the Peace Corps.

Stewie Griffin

"MY DIAPER HAS GONE OVER TO THE DARK SIDE"

There's probably no baby in the world like Stewie Griffin, an infant with a huge vocabulary who some people can understand perfectly, while others, such as his mother, only get the gist of what he's saying. With a voice like Rex Harrison, in his early day he was bent on world domination and more particularly on destroying Lois, who he tends to blame for all the world's ills.

In more recent adventures, his megalomaniacal ardour has calmed down. He's not slacking completely as his knack for gadgets and machines allows him to build things such as jet packs, time travel machines, teleportation pods and mind control devices. He also loves his teddy Rupert a little too much, as the baby with an ambiguous sexuality sometimes fantasises about Rupert having a teddy's head and a buff man's body.

Brian Griffin

"I'M NOT PICKING UP YOUR POOP."

Brian was living on the streets as a stray before Peter took pity on him and invited him into the Griffin household. He was actually born on a puppy farm in Texas and for years felt abandoned by his mother, before realising she let him go so he could have a better life (although when Brian went back home to make amends, he was horrified to find his mum had been stuffed and turned into a table).

A rather pretentious canine who likes to think he's smarter than he is, he loves opera and jazz, and after years spent working on a novel, he did finally manage to get it published – even if it hardly sold any copies.

At one point he thought he'd found his perfect match in Jillian, who was incredibly dim but they nevertheless shared a bond. Their relationship fell apart but Brian still holds a torch for her.

WELCOME TO

RHODE ISLAND ISN'T A PLACE MANY PEOPLE GO TO, PARTLY BECAUSE IT'S SO TINY!

It's the smallest of the US states, measuring just 37 miles across and 48 miles high. Indeed it's so small many US cities, such as Houston, Greater New York and Los Angeles, are bigger than the entirety of Rhode Island. It was however one of the original 13 US states. In fact it has claims to be the very first, as it declared independence from Britain two months before anyone else, in May 1776.

FAMILY GUY FACT

RHODE ISLAND ISN'T AN ISLAND. MOST OF IT'S ON THE US MAINLAND BUT IT'S NAMED AFTER AN ISLAND JUST OFF THE COAST, NOW NORMALLY KNOWN AS AQUIDNECK ISLAND.

While less than 0.5% of the US population live in Rhode Island, the state is the home of the Griffins, who live in Quahog (pronounced Ko-hog). You'll have difficulty finding the town on a map though, as it isn't a real place. It is, however, based on one. Quahog is loosely patterned on Cranston, Rhode Island,

RHODE ISLAND

Welcome To Beautiful
RHODE ISLAND

a city of 80,000 people that is pretty much a suburb of the state capitol, Providence. You can even sometimes see Providence landmarks in the background behind the Griffins' house. The name isn't made up either, as Quahog is the name of an edible clam – which is fitting as the town's founding myth says the city was started by Miles 'Chatterbox' Musket, with the assistance of a magical talking clam.

The Griffin house is on Spooner Street, which is a quiet residential area west of downtown Quahog. The Griffins live at number 31, the Swansons are at 33, while Quagmire resides in number 29. Also on the street is elderly pederast Herbert, while Cleveland Brown and his ex-wife Loretta used to live just opposite the Griffins. Rather oddly though, for some reason the plot of land Peter's house stands on was left off the official maps, meaning it wasn't a part of the United States. This allowed Peter to become president of Petoria, until he tried to invade the US by annexing Joe's pool. This caused a swift military response by the American government, who soon made Peter sign his country over to them.

FAMILY GUY FACT

THE REASON FAMILY GUY CREATOR, SETH MACFARLANE CHOSE TO SET THE SHOW IN RHODE ISLAND IS BECAUSE HE WENT TO THE RHODE ISLAND SCHOOL OF DESIGN.

GETTING TO

MEET THE GRIFFINS' FRIENDS AND NEIGHBOURS

PETER AND HIS FAMILY DON'T LIVE AN ISOLATED LIFE IN QUAHOG, AS THEY HAVE LOADS OF FRIENDS, NEIGHBOURS AND VARIOUS OTHER CHARACTERS WHO POP INTO AND OUT OF THEIR LIVES. LET'S MEET THEM!

The Swanson's

Although it feels like Joe and his family have been with us since the very beginning of Family Guy, they actually turned up five episodes in, when they moved into the house next door to the Griffins. Initially Peter was jealous that people thought Joe was a hero even though he was in a wheelchair, but they soon became firm friends.

As well as Joe there's his wife Bonnie, who for the first seven seasons of the show was pregnant, a situation that went on for so long that Peter demanded she either "Have the baby or not". Eventually baby Susie was born, a cute little girl who Stewie has a bit of a crush on. Oddly, the voice in Susie's head that we occasionally hear has a baritone English accent and sounds like Patrick Stewart! Early on the Swansons also had a teenage son called Kevin, but he was tragically killed in Iraq, or so everyone thought until Season 10!

FAMILY GUY FACT

Joe ended up in a wheelchair after becoming paralysed while attempting to stop a grinch like creature from ruining Christmas.

Glenn Quagmire

It's an understatement to say that Quagmire likes sex. Pretty much every waking moment of his life is spent either sleeping with women or trying to sleep with women – and it's occasionally been hinted a few lady-boys have slipped in there too. He will do anything to have sex, whether it's locking Asian women in his basement or drugging ladies so he can sleep with them.

While he's a complete sex hound – to the point that at one time the women of Quahog tried to have him thrown out of town – he's normally a pretty loyal friend (as long as you don't have a teenage daughter over the age of 18!), and also has an unexpected love of cats. Glenn was once briefly married to a woman called Joan, but he soon came to his senses when she became needy and neurotic. Thankfully for Glenn, Joan died after touching Death's arm. All his sleeping around also resulted in a daughter being left on his doorstep, but Quagmire decided it was best for the little girl to give her up for adoption.

Glenn hates Brian the dog with a passion, finding him pretentious and insufferable. He also reckons that the reason he's so obsessed with sex is because he's trying to fill the hole left when his ex, TV actress Cheryl Tiegs, left him. By day he's an airline pilot, which allows him to pay for all his sexual shenanigans.

FAMILY GUY FACT

Family Guy Fact: In the episode 'FOXy Lady', Glenn's driving license says he's 61 years old!

The Pewterschmidts

Lois' parents are very, very rich. They have so much money that Carter hangs out with the likes of Bill Gates and when he and Barbara briefly split up, she married the equally wealthy Ted Turner. Carter is an industrialist who owns Pewterschmidt Industries and US Steel. A stereotypical old-money US billionaire, he believes that money is at the heart of happiness and that as the oldest and richest man in the family, he's the top dog who should be in charge of everything.

As a result, the fact his daughter married an oaf – and a poor oaf at that – is a major bugbear for him. While there are occasional times when he gets along with his son-in-law, much of the time he likes nothing better than to see Peter fail.

Barbara meanwhile is more chilled out. She loves her husband and is happy with her daughter's choice of husband as long as Lois loves him and he treats her okay. That's not to say it's been all plain sailing for her and Carter. As mentioned, they briefly got divorced when he lost all his money and their marriage also nearly broke down when she discovered Carter was having an affair. She also spent years hiding a secret, as Lois was brought up thinking both her parents were protestants. However Barbara is actually a Jewish holocaust survivor, born Barbara Hebrewberg. The old-fashioned and rather racist Carter forced her to hide her heritage.

FAMILY GUY FACT

Carter is a war veteran who at one point was presumed killed in action, but luckily made it back to the US before Barbara married another man called Roginald.

Herbert

Few neighbourhoods would be as happy to have a paedophile hanging around, but the people of Quahog either don't notice Herbert's proclivities or ignore them. While he may like young boys, he's very bad at doing anything about it. Stewie has the best take on it, saying "Well, there's a paedophile up the street that nobody seems to be doing anything about, but it's mainly because he's so funny."

Despite numerous attempts to ensnare boys and his constant attempts to get Chris to remove his shirt, Herbert is too old and feeble to be a real menace. Indeed his unhealthy hebephilia (an attraction to boys in the early years of puberty) can sometimes come in handy, such as when he rescues Chris from the basement of an evil Nazi and battling a living tree in the episode 'Petergeist' so he can save the teenager.

Like Carter, Herbert is a war veteran, having served in Army Air Corps during World War II. When the Nazis captured him, he was locked up in a concentration camp because the Germans thought he was gay. He now lives up the street from the Griffins, along with his ancient, half-crippled dog, Jesse.

FAMILY GUY FACT

We first met Herbert in the season 3 episode 'To Love and Die in Dixie', when Chris starts delivering newspapers to his house.

The Goldmans

Neil Goldman was the first of Quahog's stereotypically Jewish family that we met. He spent the early days of the show chasing after Meg, declaring his love for her and not taking no for an answer, even when she very forcefully told him she wasn't interested! Eventually we met Neil's parents, Mort and Muriel, who look worryingly like one another (but hopefully aren't related).

Mort is the local pharmacist, running Goldman's Pharmacy, which is handy for him as he's a complete hypochondriac, convinced he has pretty much every ailment under the sun, to the point that he even thought he was having a miscarriage after someone scared him. He and Muriel met via a dating service, where surprisingly enough it was love at first sight! Tragically though, in Season 9 during a dinner in honour of James Woods, a murderer starts killing their way through the guest list, murdering Muriel. Since then Mort's been trying to put his life back together as a widower.

FAMILY GUY FACT

Mort and Muriel's niece is the actress Jennifer Love Hewitt.

The Channel 5 Action News Team

If you need to move a plot forward, The Channel 5 Action News Team are the guys to call on. They're always on hand with a conveniently timed news report which ensures stories can keep moving along at a brisk pace. As a result the news team play an oddly important role in the Griffin family's life.

For many years the show was anchored by Tom Tucker and Diane Simmons. However in Season 9, Diane discovered she was about to be fired and so concocted an elaborate plan to kill her love, James Woods, and frame Tom for the crime, eventually murdering several other people in an attempt to escape blame. While she nearly got away with it, Lois realised Diane was the killer. Diane tried to kill Lois, but Stewie shot her, with her body falling into the ocean. As a result, Joyce Kinney was brought in as the new co-anchor. Tom

Tucker meanwhile has a son called Jake who has an upside-down face and also had a bit of a penchant for sleeping with hookers.

Alongside the hosts, there's the monosyllabic Ollie Williams, who presents the 'Blaccu-Weather Forecast', normally by shouting things like, "It gon' rain!" Some reports come via Maria Jimenez and human interest reporter Dirk Bandit, but the best known is the fearless Asian reporter Tricia Takanawa, who will do pretty much anything to get a story!

FAMILY GUY FACT

In 'One if by Clam, Two if by Sea', Ollie Williams was briefly replaced by Greg the Weather Mime.

Bruce

If there's a job going in Quahog, it's probably going to be filled by Bruce. He's known as Bruce the performance artist, but he was first seen behind the desk of a horror novelty

shop. The rather softly spoken, moustachioed gent taught a CPR course, has been a member of the School board, a psychic, a verger, worked in a bowling alley, a lawyer, bartender, referee, therapist, and leads an AA meeting, amongst other things. If that weren't enough, in fantasy cutaways he has also been everything from a bee to a camp version of Jaws. Bruce is almost certainly gay and in a relationship with a man called Jeffrey, who we never see.

FAMILY GUY FACT

In 'The Splendid Source', we discover Bruce has a pet rabbit called Steven.

Seamus

Life has not been easy for Seamus, although quite how he got to be a man with two wooden peg legs, two wooden peg arms and blind in one eye is a bit mysterious. The salty old sea dog once suggested his father was a tree, which was backed up in the episode, 'Ocean's Three And A Half', where we see his body is wooden too and only his head is human. However in 'And Then There Were Fewer', it appears Seamus was once a normal person until he got high with James Woods, who ended up eating his arms and legs!

The seafarer is often around, ready to warn Peter of the dangers that may await him, as well as going for unexpected jobs, such as the church organist and a news reporter.

FAMILY GUY FACT

Bizarrely, rolled up in one of his wooden arms Seamus keeps a picture of a diseased prostate, a cat doing pull ups, a map of Middle Earth, and an image of the band Primus, as revealed in the episode 'Stewie Loves Lois'.

The Giant

Chicken

Not many people have an ongoing feud with a giant chicken, but Peter does. It all started when the chicken gave Peter an expired coupon. Peter then attacked the chicken, resulting in an elaborate battle that ended with the huge fowl falling from an office building, with Peter landing on him. However that wasn't the end of the fight, as over the years Peter and the massive bird have continued to fight on-and-off.

At one point it seemed all would be forgiven when Peter and the giant chicken realise they can't even remember what they are fighting about. However at the end of a reconciliatory meal, they fall out over the check and begin their battle all over again! It's difficult to know whether the whole thing is Peter or the chicken's fault, as even when Peter has lost his memory he manages to inadvertently anger the bird so much that the animal ends up hitting the amnesia right out of Peter's head! It's undoubtedly a feud that will run and run.

FAMILY GUY FACT

When not fighting Peter, the giant chicken lives in a normal house with his wife, Nicole.

EPISODE GUIDE

IT'S A BIT ODD THAT IT'S TAKEN 13 YEARS FOR FAMILY GUY TO REACH SEASON 10, BUT THE SHOW WAS FAMOUSLY CANCELLED FOR A COUPLE OF YEARS, BEFORE BEING BROUGHT BACK BY POPULAR DEMAND. AS A RESULT IT'S TAKEN US SLIGHTLY LONGER TO GET TO SEASON 10 THAN IT SHOULD HAVE, BUT THE SHOW IS STILL GOING STRONG.

SEASON 10

With 23 new episodes, there's loads more lunacy with the Griffins. After all, what other family would agree to have a dolphin come and live with them, or end up getting in a war with the Amish? There's plenty of drama for everyone, with Brian falling in love with a blind girl, Meg turning 18 (which certainly excites Quagmire), Peter and his friends getting locked up in a Southern prison, Chris starting to date someone who looks exactly like Lois, and Stewie getting into not just one car crash but two.

We've got your full guide to the complete season, covering every crazy turn and nutty mishap, from Peter and Chris going to fat camp, to the reappearance of a character everyone thought was dead. Even 10 seasons on, we're lucky there's a man who positively can do all the things that make us laugh and cry. He's a Family Guy.

LOTTERY FEVER

Money will go to your head

Peter wants to open a sushi restaurant but that age old problem – money – stands in his way. Lois says the family is living on the edge and they're all going to have to survive on a tight budget from now on. That doesn't sound much fun to Peter, who comes up with what he thinks is a foolproof plan to get more cash. The lottery!

With the jackpot at $50 million, the Griffin patriarch remortgages the house and buys 200,000 lottery tickets, convinced he's going to win. Brian and the others aren't so confident, with Lois telling her hubby, "When we lose, I'm getting a divorce."

Peter's confidence is undimmed though, getting the whole family to spend days sorting through the thousands of tickets (as well as checking 400,000 dummy tickets Peter had printed for practice!) Incredibly though, and despite the odds, the Griffins win, with Peter declaring, "Yes! We won the lottery! I'm getting a penis butler."

Peter cashes the check, leaving millions of dollars in cash lying around his house, convinced that, "This is awesome. Now that we're rich, our lives are going to be so much better."

But what are they gonna spend the cash on? Chris says, "I'm going to get some supermarket fried chicken and eat it until I'm nauseous." Stewie has different plans, "I'm going to finally get my gal that doodad she's been wantin'!". Meg meanwhile reckons, "I'm going to get a floor mirror to squat over and see what's making all that noise."

Lois is quick to calm everyone down, as she realises they need to be sensible. "We're not going to go crazy spending our winnings," she says, "and we're not going to let this money change us."

Peter doesn't listen to his wife though, immediately quitting his job and spending his time at the Drunken Clam buying drinks for everybody. However now that Peter's rolling in moolah, his friends soon start trying to get him to give them some of it. Glenn wants money to invest in a penis enlargement pill business and Joe asks Peter to pay for Stevie Nicks to come to his house and sing three songs to Bonnie for her birthday.

With all his cash, Peter doesn't mind sharing the wealth with his friends a little. They're not getting the money completely without strings though, telling his mates, "From now on, we're all gonna do whatever I want to do. 'Cause I'm the one with dough." With their pockets full of Griffin cash, Joe and Quagmire agree.

Peter starts getting people to do odd errands for him, such as Joe watching True Blood just to find out when you can see a boob and getting Glenn to take the first bite of an ice lolly in the hope that means he won't get an ice headache. With Peter's propensity to take things to the extreme, it's not long before he's pushing people to the limit. The breaking point comes when he forces Joe and Quagmire to do a synchronised duet of the song 'Makin' Whoopee', while being shot at with a BB gun!

After Peter shoots Joe in the eye, the policeman has had enough and tells his friend so. The Griffin dad can't see the problem – surely if he gives people money, they should do whatever he wants, right? Joe and Glenn don't see it that way, walking out on Peter and telling him, "Go to hell, Peter! We don't need your money! And we don't need friends like you!"

Despite losing his friends, Peter continues spending the cash, convinced that money is all he needs to be happy. But with Peter buying things like a solid gold tuxedo, Stewie splashing out on a giant mobile he can hang in the sky, Lois getting huge diamonds and the family not thinking twice about paying for things like giving a lobster a helicopter ride, they start getting through the money really fast.

While out at a posh country club, Peter's card is declined because he blown all his cash! Not learning his lesson, Peter's first instinct is to try the lottery again, and while miraculously he wins a second time, the Griffins keep on spending and blow through $150 million in a month! Now they've got no money and no friends, although Lois is convinced Joe and Quagmire are good people. "They'll listen," she says. "And they'll care what happens to us, even after everything that's happened."

It seems Peter's learned his lesson this time though, as he gives the guys a big apology, telling them, "Winning the lottery was the worst thing that ever happened to me and my family. I thought being rich would solve all my problems, but all it did was make me forget what was important. Like who my real friends are. I don't expect you to forgive me, but if, for some reason, you do, you can find me in a cardboard box on the corner of Meeting and Thayer."

Despite their argument Quagmire and Joe aren't about to see their friend out on the street, with Glenn offering some of the money he made from the penis enlargement pills to help the Griffins out and get their house back. In the end, Lois is convinced that, "Despite all the ups and downs, things turned out for the best. I mean, really, we're no worse off than we were before. Plus, we learned something. And you can't put a price on that."

SEAHORSE SEASHELL PARTY

A hurricane inside and outside the Griffin house!

Hurricane Flozell is due to hit Quahog and everybody has been urged to stay indoors for at least 36 hours. That includes the Griffins, who've holed themselves up in their house, with Peter hoping he'll at least have the TV to help pass the time – except that the hurricane knocks out the satellite dish. It may be the most difficult day and a half of the family's lives, as they've only got each other to talk to!

Brian thinks he's got a good plan to pass the time during the hurricane – take hallucinogenic mushrooms! Stewie finds out what the dog is about to do, pretending he's okay with people taking drugs. "Oh yeah, I'm totally cool about that," he says. "I-I-I-I have a lot of friends who do it, and they're willing to do it around me all the time, because they know I'm so cool about it and I don't judge them. So, you know, go a-head..."

With the storm raging outside the rest of the family are bored and try to find ways to pass the time. Charades doesn't work as Peter can't mime things without saying what he's doing, and while the family try to play finger-bang (pretending your fingers are

gun barrels), nobody wants Meg to finger-bang them.

Brian meanwhile is starting to feel the effects of the mushrooms, seeing Chris turning purple, Stewie's head changing shape, Meg becoming a cowboy and Peter suddenly wearing a grass skirt and dancing the hula! The dog's trip starts turning bad when Stewie discovers him in front of the bathroom mirror, holding a pair of scissors to his ear and declaring, "I'm gonna cut my ear off to prevent World War Two."

Stewie tries to stop Brian but he's too late and the canine lops his ear off! Brian is still messed up by the mushrooms and doesn't seem that bothered, saying strange things like "Lesbians and deaf women wear the same clothes". Stewie is freaking out though, vowing to stay by Brian's side all night to make sure he doesn't do anything else that's dangerous.

In the living room, Peter is still trying to find things to do, such as humming the opening music to Indiana Jones And The Last Crusade. However he stops because he thinks it's Meg who's the one being annoying. It's the straw that broke the camel's back for Meg, who's had enough of years of being treated

badly by her family, screaming "I am sick of all you guys ganging up on me! You guys all think you're so much better than me!"

Brian's mushroom trip is getting worse. Stewie tries to calm him down, but the hallucinations are taking a nasty turn. The dog starts to think the baby is a monster who's trying to maim him, skeleton hands reach out of the darkness to get him and a cockroach with Meg's head emerges! Eventually Brian is completely lost in a strange world he's hallucinating, with Peter being roasted on a spit and Lois being scary and sexy at the same time. Eventually though Stewie manages to snap Brian back into reality and they go to get the dehydrated doggie a drink.

Meg meanwhile is continuing to tell her family why she thinks they're bastards. Lois thinks Meg is just being dramatic, telling her, "Look, the bottom line here, Meg, is that you're just taking your own problems out on everyone else."

It's the other way around for Meg though, who tells her mom, "Is this coming from my role model mother? The shoplifter, the drug addict, the porn star, the whore who let Gene Simmons and Bill Clinton go to town on her? My point is that with all the irresponsible, reckless, idiotic behaviour in your past, that somehow, somehow you have the nerve, the arrogance to consistently and ruthlessly point out my shortcomings."

Meg continues her tirade about her mother's inadequacies, ending with the heartbreaking, "You're my mother, and you took a child's trust and smashed it into bits in a 17-year-long mission to destroy something that you killed a long time ago. And honestly, when I turn 18...I-I don't know that I ever want to see you again." Lois finally breaks down and cries, realising that she has been cruel to her daughter.

Trying to apologise to her daughter, Lois says, "Oh, Meg, I don't know what to say. All of those things you said about me are true. I have been a very bad mother to you. I have no excuse. I just have this horrible, overwhelming desire to point out faults in you. I don't know where it comes from. Maybe it's because I'm self-conscious about being a bad parent. I'm just, I'm so disgusted with my behaviour. And I'm so sorry, Meg."

However Meg hasn't finished yet, yelling at Peter about his shortcomings as a father and telling him how he's completely wasted his life. Soon everyone is at each other's throats, with Peter, Lois and Chris screaming at each other.

Having recovered from his rather scary mushroom trip, Brian tells Meg, "You know, that was, uh, that was pretty cool the way you finally stood up to everybody." However Meg has realised that without her to pick on, her family has turned on one another like a pack of wolves.

"Do you think it's possible," Meg asks Brain, "That this family can't survive without some sort of lightning rod to absorb all the dysfunction? ... Maybe if I feel bad, they don't have to."

She decides to selflessly take on the role of being the family punching bad, telling her parents they're actually really good and she's was just taking out her frustrations on them. Glad to have Meg back to hate rather than looking at their own shortcomings, family harmony re-emerges, with the Griffins' only daughter oddly happy to be called a bitch.

SCREAMS OF SILENCE: THE STORY OF BRENDA Q.

Violence is never the answer!

Peter is going fishing for the weekend with Joe and Quagmire, but feels a bit annoyed that Glenn is late to the boat. He and Joe decide to go over to Quagmire's house to find out what's keeping him. They open the door to the house to find Glenn hanging from the ceiling, with the boys realising that Quagmire must have autoerotically asphyxiated himself while watching clown porn!

Thankfully though, Glenn isn't dead but he is in a coma. As a result, Quagmire's sister Brenda and her boyfriend, Jeff, come to town to look after him. Lois isn't happy to hear this, as she knows Jeff has a reputation for beating Brenda. Jeff's just as horrible as Lois believes, constantly putting Brenda down and calling her names, not seeming to care that her brother is in a coma. He even belittles her attempts to help her brother wake-up, saying "Come on, Brenda, a stupid nursery rhyme isn't going to wake him up, especially the way you sing."

Miraculously though Brenda's singing works and Glenn comes round. Jeff immediately thinks this means they can go, but Brenda wants to stay to look after her brother. Unsurprisingly, Jeff isn't happy about this and starts being increasingly unreasonable, screaming at his girlfriend and criticising everything about her, no matter whether it makes any sense or not.

After Quagmire gets out of the hospital he can't get any sleep as Jeff and Brenda argue all night. Glenn isn't sure what to do about it, telling Peter and Lois, "I've tried talking to Brenda about leaving him, but I haven't gotten anywhere. I was actually hoping you could talk to her, Lois. She might open up more to you, you know, 'cause you're a woman."

Lois isn't sure about this, but eventually agrees, taking Brenda to a café to have a chat. Wearing sunglasses to hide her black eye, Brenda tells Lois that at home she's not allowed to have female friends as Jeff won't allow it. Lois is most horrified by the black

eye, but Brenda tries to reassure her, saying "No, I-it's really not that bad. It only hurts when I see."

Lois can't understand why Brenda stays with Jeff, but Glenn's sister defends her boyfriend, convinced that, "Oh, Jeff's sweet. You don't see how soft and gentle he hits me when we're alone." Jeff has convinced Brenda that everything she does is wrong and that she deserves to be belittled and hit, and Lois can't get her to see it any other way.

The boys meanwhile are looking for an answer of their own, as Quagmire can't bear to see his sister being abused. Peter thinks Joe should just arrest Jeff, but the police can't get involved unless Brenda makes an official complaint. "She won't go to the police," Glenn says, "She's afraid of what Jeff will do. And to be honest, I don't blame her. I mean, what happens if one of these nights, he hits her so hard he kills her?" The only other answer they can come up with is staging an intervention to try and convince Brenda to face her problems.

This doesn't go well though, such as Meg giving Brenda the less than helpful advice, "I feel like if he likes you, maybe you can change him", and Peter getting confused between trying to get Brenda to leave Jeff and trying to stop a teenager from smoking. Unsurprisingly Brenda isn't convinced by their efforts, and even a moving, impassioned speech from her brother won't change her mind. Indeed far from leaving Jeff, she announces they're getting married because she's pregnant!

The news makes Quagmire frantic, as he can't let Brenda marry such a brute. The boys come up with a drastic plan – kill Jeff! Joe doesn't think murder is the answer, but Glenn can't think of any other answer, as "These kinds of guys don't change. You think they ever suddenly wake up and realize the error of their ways

and clean up their act? No! They just keep ruining everyone's lives, and the world is better off without 'em." Joe's still not sure, but when he sees Jeff slap Brenda, he agrees to go along with it.

Glenn, Joe and Peter invite Jeff out with them on a midnight hunting trip. Once out in the woods Jeff realises what's happening and pulls out a gun, taking Quagmire hostage and driving off, leaving Joe and Peter to freeze in the woods.

Jeff tells Quagmire he's going to kill him and make it look like a hunting accident. Glenn manages to convince Jeff they should have a fist fight and so they begin having a massive brawl. It seems Jeff has won when he chokes Quagmire. However Glenn chokes himself every day and so he's used to it and was just pretending to be dead. He manages to get into the car and smashes it into Jeff, killing him.

Brenda is distraught, but the boys come up with a fake letter from Jeff explaining why he left. It certainly has to be better than Brenda being hit all the time!

STEWIE GOES FOR A DRIVE
Now I can do a slow cruise past my ex-girlfriend's apartment!

Peter's feeling pleased with himself for being brave at the doctors when a car pulls up to them and the guy inside says he's lost. The Griffins can hardly believe it because the man in the car is the movie star, Ryan Reynolds! After giving him directions, Ryan drives off and the rather starstruck Griffins never expect to see him again.

Meanwhile, Brian drives Stewie back from daycare. Once at the house, Stewie says he wants to stay in the car to listen to the end of a song he likes. However the baby accidentally hits the gear stick and moves the automatic into drive before pulling the car to a stop almost immediately. Stewie is elated, "Oh, my God. I just drove. That was amazing. I can drive! Now I can do a slow cruise past my ex-girlfriend's apartment!"

Lois and Peter are surprised to find that their encounter with Ryan Reynolds won't be their last, as he's in town to shoot a movie and has decided to rent the house across the street from the Griffins. It also appears Ryan wants to be in Quahog so he can hang out with Peter, and perhaps more unexpectedly, flirt with him, saying things like, "Okay, I'm embarrassed. I'm standing out here without a shirt on and my pajama bottoms are riding insanely low on my hips."

Stewie hasn't forgotten the exhilaration of his accidental driving adventure and so sneaks out with his teddy Rupert and sets off in the car. However Stewie is overconfident in his driving skills as he's

hardly been on the road any time when he gets distracted by a radio competition and crashes into a road light. "Oh, my God. Oh, my God. Oh, my God, Brian's gonna be so mad at me," Stewie says frantically to Rupert. "What am I gonna do? Okay, it's all right. I'll just get a little bit of paint and cover up the dents. Unattractive women do it all the time."

Ryan is having a housewarming party and while Peter assumed his invitation also extended to Lois, the movie star isn't that keen on having Peter's wife around. It doesn't stop Ryan from flirting with Peter though, such as pointing out how tight his t-shirt is, and asking him, "So what's all this about, everyone in

Quahog likes to tickle fight?" Peter's not the smartest of people and so thinks that maybe having tickle fights with Ryan Reynolds isn't that weird. Ryan asks Peter to go out on Thursday night, making it sound a bit like a date, but Peter doesn't seem to realise that and agrees.

Despite Stewie's attempts to cover up the damage, Brian sees the dent in his car almost immediately. Stewie tries to say it doesn't have anything to do with him, but he's left Rupert in the car and so Brian knows it was him. "I can't believe you drove my car!" Brian tells him. "You could have gotten yourself killed! I'm gonna have to tell Peter and Lois." Stewie frantically tries to get Brian to change his mind, but the dog is adamant.

Peter and Ryan have gone out for dinner, which is yet another opportunity for the star to flirt with Peter and get the Griffin patriarch to notice his body. The flirting does get slightly odd though, such as Ryan saying, "Hey, have you noticed what a jerk the mailman is in this town? Like, he said there is no way Peter Griffin could crush a baby bird with his bare foot while I watched." When it gets to the point that Ryan is trying to feed Peter by hand, the fat man realises that maybe the movie star's intentions aren't purely platonic.

Stewie is panicking about Brian telling his parents about the crash as he knows he's going to be in huge amounts of trouble. He decides that his only option is to run away and so he heads off to the airport, leaving a note explaining his decision to Brian!

Not realising their baby is missing, Peter thinks his main problem is Ryan's infatuation with him, although Lois refuses to believe that can possibly be true. "It's true," Peter insists, "Last night we were at this restaurant, and he tried to gay kiss me. I'm telling you, he wants to get with me."

Peter decides that his best course of action is to let Ryan down easily, which proves harder than he expected because as soon as he hints to Ryan that he thinks he's gay, the movie star gets offended. He explains, "Peter, I'm not gay. What the hell's the matter with you? Look, look, look, let me...let me put it to you this way. I'm attracted to you in the way that a man is attracted to a woman, but I'm not gay... I just thought maybe our spirits could intertwine, you know? Our energies could merge. Like my spirit could go up inside your energy." However he doesn't like labels and tells Peter to leave.

Running away wasn't as easy as Stewie thought, as before he could get to the airport Consuela the maid found him, decided he'd be her baby now and took him home. Brian uses his super-sensitive nose to track him down but Stewie still doesn't want to go home and get in trouble. However Brian has decided not to tell Lois and Peter about the crash and so Stewie agrees to go home. Consuela doesn't want to let him go, but after Stewie shoots her in the foot, she doesn't have much choice!

FAMILY GUY

GETTING A CLUE IN QUAHOG

HAVE YOU GOT A CLUE? IF SO, HERE'S OUR FIENDISH FAMILY GUY CROSSWORD, WHERE ALL THE ANSWERS HAVE SOMETHING TO DO WITH THE AWESOME ANIMATED SHOW.

DOWN

1 Surname of Action 5 News' Asian Correspondent (8)
3 US State the show is set in (5,6)
4 Voice of Joe (7,9)
5 Wife of the Griffin's policeman neighbour (6)
7 Family Guy patriarch (5,7)
9 Family Guy creator (4,10)
13 Lois' maiden name (13)
14 First name of Lois' homicidal brother (7)
15 Teenage son of the Griffin family (5)
17 Voice of Lois (4,8)
18 Name of the brewery where Peter works (9,7)
19 Lois' father's first name (6)
21 Elderly pederast Griffin neighbour (7)
23 Christian name of the Griffins' teen daughter (5)
27 Name of Brian's gay cousin (6)
28 Channel 5's Blaccu Weather Forecaster (5,8)
29 Family Guy's Jewish pharmacist (4,7)
30 Wheelchair using Griffin neighbour (3,7)
31 Stewie's middle name (8)
32 Stewie's favourite teddy bear (6)
34 Youngest member of the Griffin brood (6)
35 First name of the person Peter thought was his father when he was growing up (7)
36 Herbert's dog (5)

ACROSS

2 Action 5 News' male anchor (3,6)
6 Town Family Guy is set in (6)
8 The Griffins' talking dog (5)
10 Woman who replaced Diane Simmons as the female anchor of Action 5 news (5,6)
11 Stewie's half-brother and mortal enemy (7)
12 Voice of Meg (4,5)
16 First name of Lois' mother (7)
20 Country where Peter was born (6)
22 Joe's baby daughter (5)
23 Quahog's civic leader and now Lois' brother-in-law (5,4)
24 African-American former Griffin neighbour (9,5)
25 Type of animal that used to live in Chris' closet (6)
26 Family guys' Mexican maid character (8)
29 First name of the deceased wife of Peter' Jewish pharmacist friend (6)
33 Sex mad neighbour of the Griffins (5,8)
37 Road on which the Griffins live (7,6)
38 Peter's mother's Christian name (6)
39 Name of Peter's biological father (6,10)
40 Voice of Chris (4,5)

CROSSWORD

SO IF YOU KNOW WHAT PETER'S MOTHER'S CHRISTIAN NAME IS AND WHO VOICES MEG, YOU'LL HAVE A BIT OF A HEAD START ON BEING ABLE TO FILL IN THE GRID.

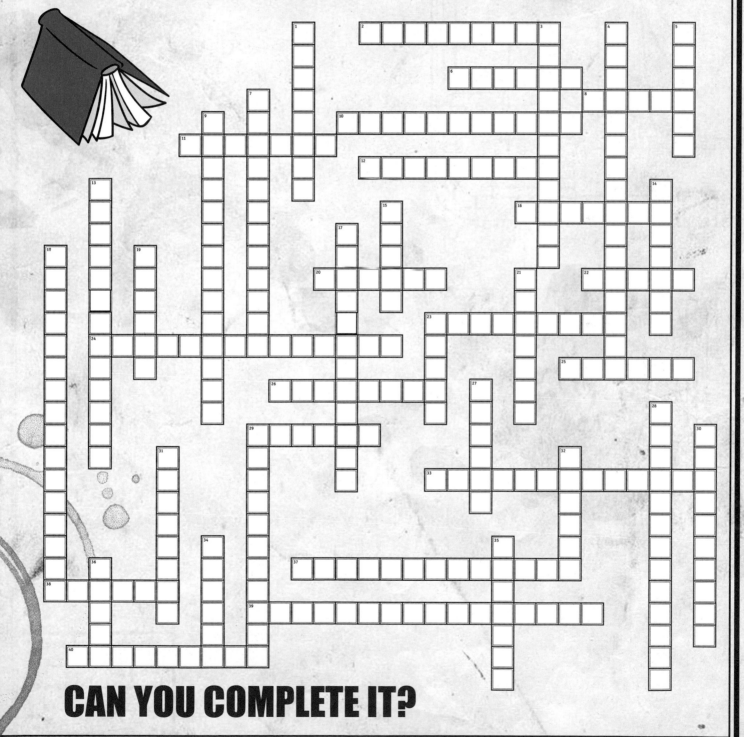

CAN YOU COMPLETE IT?

BACK TO THE PILOT

Remembering the early days of Family Guy

Brian is annoyed because he can't remember where he buried a particularly awesome tennis ball that he peed on. Stewie doesn't see this as problem, as he's got a time travel machine. Brian knows he buried the ball on January 31st, 1999 – the same day the very first episode of Family guy aired on American TV.

Once back in the past, Stewie sums things up saying, "That's odd. It's our house, but somehow it looks a little different." Inside, the very first events we ever saw of the Griffin family are unfolding, with Meg asking for collagen injections and Stewie from the past working on a mind control device.

Brian quickly sees where he buried the ball and goes to dig it up. Stewie tells him he can't do that, because they can't do anything that would alter the past. "You know, I never got that," says Brian. "I mean, wouldn't you want to alter the past? I mean, you could make life better for yourself. And not just for yourself, for everyone. You could stop 9/11."

Stewie is certain though, "Brian, there's one rule of time travel, and that is: Do not alter the past in any way or the consequences could be dire." Not wanting to change the past, they just watch their family telling jokes and setting up cutaway gags. Brian says he needs to take a pee before they go back to the present and so heads out of the room.

While Brian's gone, the Stewie from the past discover the present-day Stewie hiding under his bed. At first he refuses to believe his future self has time-travelled, but his doppelganger knows things only the real Stewie would know. The baby knows he has to get out of the past before he changes things too much, but there's not enough juice in the return pad, and so he and Brian end up at the stadium where the 1999 Super Bowl is taking place. Brian remembers he was up in the sky at the time, flying a blimp, and that Peter is about to throw money on the crowd. That turns out to be a good thing, as they need more cash for batteries.

The falling cash causes pandemonium, with people firing into the air. The bullets hit the blimp

and cause it to crash. While the airship is about to land on Stewie and Brian, thankfully they manage to time travel just before it hits them. They're still in 1999 though, at a time when Peter is in court for having cashed a huge cheque the government accidentally sent him. Stewie and Brian watch the court case for a while, but soon realise they need to get back home and so head off to buy batteries.

Once in the present day, it quickly becomes apparent that despite Stewie's warnings, someone must have altered the past. Lois calls to Brian to come and watch the news so he can see the unveiling of a statue of him. Brian is confused and asks what the statue is for, with Lois explaining, "What do you think, Mr. National Hero? For stopping the 9/11 terrorist attacks and saving our country."

It turns out that when Brian went off for a pee in the past, he told his former self about 9/11, allowing him to prevent the attacks. "Brian, you shouldn't have done that," says Stewie. "Who knows what unforeseen consequences are awaiting us. Saddam Hussein could be president. Mexico could be the world's dominant super power. Cookie Monster could have invented Facebook!"

Brian isn't worried though, convinced that saving 3,000 lives can't be a bad thing! However the newsreader interrupts to announce, "This major breaking news just in. Nine Southern states have declared that they are seceding from the United States. The announcement came from former President George W. Bush, who reformed the Confederacy after a bitter

loss in his 2004 re-election bid."

With no 9/11 to use, President Bush never got a second term, and now the country is at war, all because of Brian! The dog still thinks things could turn out okay, and so he and Stewie travel five years into the future, where people need armour and guns just to get across the road and Quagmire has mutated into a frog due to the nuclear fallout from bombs that killed 17 million people. It's clear the dog and baby need to go back to 1999 and make sure 9/11 happens! Using the time machine they head back, with Brian telling the version of himself from a few hours ago not to spill the beans about the New York terrorist attacks.

Once back in the present day, it seems things have worked, as 9/11 happened, but this time Brian has told his former self about Harry Potter, so he's now the author of the fantasy books. As a result they must go back to the past once more to sort it out, but once there, more and more versions of themselves turn up, all there to prevent the various previous versions from doing things that affect the future.

Uncertain what to do, Stewie eventually decides all the Stewies and Brians should have a vote over whether to stop 9/11 or not, eventually deciding that it should happen and that everyone must go back to where they came from and not tell anything to anyone in the past. There's just one thing left to do, which is to travel a few minutes further back in time, to stop the first time travelling Stewie and Brian from going into the house at all. With that done, normality is restored!

THANKSGIVING
Joe's son is back from the dead!

It's Thanksgiving in Quahog and the Griffins are getting ready to welcome their guests, including Joe and Bonnie, who have found the American holiday difficult ever since their son Kevin was killed in Iraq on Thanksgiving several years before. Also invited are Lois' parents, her sister Carol and Carol's new husband, Mayor West, along with Quagmire and his dad, Ida, who had a sex-change operation 18 months ago, something Glenn's still not completely comfortable with.

They all sit down to dinner and try to have a good time. There's some awkwardness though, not least between Brian and Quagmire's dad, Ida, who had a brief relationship before the dog discovered Ida had been born a man. However things seem to be going pretty well until a man walks in and causes everyone to gasp – it's Kevin, who everyone thought was dead!

Bonnie and Joe can't believe it, their son is alive. Keen to hear what happened, everyone listens to Kevin's story, where he tells them how he and his comrades were in a bunker about to tuck into a Thanksgiving dinner when they realised the trays they were eating from were actually bombs in disguise. The explosion killed everybody, except for Kevin, who

was left in a coma. However his commanding officer decided to tell Joe and Bonnie he was dead, as he wasn't expected to recover. Kevin finishes saying, "I spent five years in a Kuwait military hospital. I woke up from the coma last week, and I flew straight here. Kind of a Thanksgiving surprise."

While Joe is delighted to have his son back, he quickly starts to realise something is amiss, as Kevin claims to have seen The Hurt Locker, a movie that came out after he supposedly went into a coma. Kevin also says he didn't want his Purple Heart medal and threw it over the White House fence, something he couldn't have done if he only woke up from a coma a week ago and then came straight to Quahog. When his story changes from the bomb killing all his bunkmates to killing one and crippling the others, Joe knows there's something fishy going on and demands the truth. "Fine! Here's the truth," says Kevin, "I was never in any coma, okay? I bailed. I faked my death and went AWOL." Joe, being the upright police office he is, tells his son he's under arrest!

Bonnie wants to understand how Kevin could do what he's done, but Joe doesn't care, saying "There's nothing to understand. Our son is a deserter. Come on,

Kevin, I'm taking you to jail." He does agree to allow his son to explain himself first though.

Kevin says that while he agreed with the war to begin with, he began to change his mind. "I saw what we were doing to the people of Iraq," Kevin says. "Innocent people. There was one that I'll never forget. He was a little Iraqi street kid. I'd befriended him a few months earlier. Couldn't have been more than 12 years old. I taught him how to crack wise, American style. We bring in this civilian who got killed in the crossfire. I pull back the sheet, and who is it? Not the kid, but, like, the kid's dad's, like, coworker's neighbour. He was 74 and he had actually tried to rape someone. But just looking down at his dead face and knowing that he lived near someone who worked with the dad of the kid whose name I never found out, I lost all hope. That's when I knew I had to get out of Iraq. I just had to wait for my chance."

When the Thanksgiving bomb went off, Kevin managed to escape injury, but his bunkmates were blown into so many pieces he knew the army would never be able to prove his body wasn't there too, and so he went AWOL. He then spent some time travelling around the world, before deciding he missed the people he loved too much and came home. Most of the people in the Griffins house feel Kevin was a traitor and a coward, but the young man thinks he did the right thing, saying "I walked away from an illegal war of aggression being fought 6,000 miles away from our shores."

Brian is the only one who agrees with Kevin, although he thinks that Ida, as a military veteran herself, may agree with them. He's wrong though, as Ida feels, "Son, when you go to war, you don't end up fighting for your country or your family or your flag. You're fighting for your fellow soldiers there in the foxhole with you. You walked out on those men, and that's what's most unforgivable."

Joe is still ready to take his son to jail, but Kevin reminds him of a moment when his dad allowed a thief to escape because the criminal was only stealing to feed his destitute family. Kevin says to Joe, "You know what you were doing that day, Dad? You were breaking the law. You knew what your duty told you you were supposed to do, but instead, you did what you thought was right."

After thinking about it, Joe agrees not to take his son to jail, accepting that Kevin was only doing what he thought was right.

AMISH GUY

Could someone actually fall in love with Meg?

During a trip to a theme park, Peter is embarrassed when he's told he can't go on a rollercoaster because he's too fat. However Peter knows a new, awesome coaster is opening at another park and becomes determined to get thin enough to be allowed to go on it. Peter's diet doesn't go well though, as he thinks rice cakes are disgusting and he doesn't have any willpower. But he still wants to go on the ride! Peter thinks he's got the answer, a girdle, which allows him to look thinner while not actually losing weight.

The Griffins set off to the park in Ohio and Peter's plan works, with the man in charge of the huge new coaster letting him on the ride. The train only gets partway up the first hill before the extra weight causes it to come crashing back down into the station, killing some of the riders. Despite it being completely Peter's fault, all he takes from the experience is, "Well, this has given me a lot to think about."

On the way home the car breaks down and Lois realises that as it's Friday, there's a good chance they might not be able to get back on the road until Monday, which means a weekend in the backwards-living

Amish country. Thankfully, the Amish are welcoming to the Griffins in their hour of need.

Meg isn't impressed by the fact the Amish shun modern technology, but then she meet Eli! The boy offers to show her around, even though for him the Amish idea of a fun time is doing chores and watching other people do chores. While they're very different people, Meg can't help but respond to the fact that unlike pretty much everyone else she knows, Eli is nice to her, and so she lets him have her iPhone so he can hear some modern music.

Eli's father, Ezekiel, isn't impressed with his son spending time with an outsider, convinced that Meg will try to corrupt him. He tells his son, "You are not to see this girl again. Do you understand? I forbid it." He then turns to Meg and adds, "And, as for you, I suggest you stay away from my son, you harlot."

After finding someone who actually seems to like her, Meg is upset that Ezekiel has banned her from seeing Eli. Peter's not impressed either, but isn't sure whether he'll be able to do anything about it.

Peter finds Ezekiel at an Amish barn-raising,

where they're about to pray – "Dear Amish Lord, thou looketh sternly down upon us thine flock, even though we did not do anything wrong and have been doing chores like crazy, please make us humble, and deliver us more hardship, that we may get thick, calloused hands, much larger than other people's ... We solemnly believe that although humans have been around for a million years, you feel strongly that they had just the right amount of technology between 1835 and 1850; not too little, not too much. Please deliver us from Thomas Edison, the worst human being who ever lived. And protect us from those who laugh at our buggies or our hats and deliver us from moustaches. Amen."

Peter manages to change Ezekiel's mind after telling him that perhaps rather than corrupting Eli, Meg might want to become Amish herself. Peter then ruins everything by trying to introduce rock 'n' roll to the Amish, only to discover the song 'Highway To Hell' is enough to get him and his family banished!

The Amish form a posse, intent on getting the Griffins out of town, especially after Ezekiel discovers Meg's iPhone in Eli's corn hole! The Amish are so keen to get rid of the Griffins that even though their car isn't fixed, they've harnessed two horses to it just to get the family and their corrupting influence back on the road.

Meg's upset as, "Eli was the best boy I'll ever meet. And now I'll never see him again." She's wrong though, as her boyfriend has stowed away in the car. He declares to Meg, "I could not let you leave without me, Meg. I love you."

Lois doesn't think running away is the answer, but Eli couldn't bear the idea of never seeing Meg again. Things get more serious when Eli's father declares a

feud by graffiting the Griffins' house. Ezekiel even mows the lawn and rakes the leaves, as he believes, "Ha-ha! I have done your chores to rob you of the joy of doing chores."

Peter rounds up his friends and all the modern technology he can find and head off to war with the Amish. After being attacked with apples and surrounded by quilters, Peter fights back with a machine gun, before deciding to sort things out with a man-to-man fight with Ezekiel.

Eli manages to bring his father to his senses though, saying "Will you listen to me for one moment? You were so worried about these outsiders coming into our community and corrupting me. But look at yourself. You're the one who's allowed yourself to be corrupted."

While Ezekiel agrees his son must make his own choices, he's surprised to hear Eli choose to stay in Amish country, as while he loves Meg, he belongs in his own world. While Meg is sad, she and Eli agree they can always be friends.

WHAT'S THE

TOP FAMILY GUY QUOTES

PETER AND HIS FAMILY DON'T LIVE AN ISOLATED LIFE IN QUAHOG, AS THEY HAVE LOADS OF FRIENDS, NEIGHBOURS AND VARIOUS OTHER CHARACTERS WHO POP INTO AND OUT OF THEIR LIVES. LET'S MEET THEM!

PETER: "Lois, this family believes in the Easter bunny. He died for our sins in that helicopter crash."

EP | Family Goy

STEWIE: Heavens, it appears my wee-wee has been stricken with rigor mortis.

EP | Peter Griffin: Husband, Father... Brother?

PETER: I have an idea. An idea so smart, my head would explode if I even began to know what I was talking about."

EP | Lethal Weapons

CHRIS: (on phone)
So, what are you wearing? Wow, I bet you could see right through that.
LOIS: Chris, who are you talking to?
CHRIS: Grandma.

EP | Brian In Love

STEWIE: Come on, discipline me! Make me wear panties, rub dirt in my eye, violate me with a wine bottle! My God, I really do have problems, don't I?

EP | Peter's Two Dads

LOIS: Kids, we just have to learn to accept this. Like one of those stories on Dateline where a family member suffers a horrible accident and becomes a burden on everybody. Sure, they pretend to be happy, but they're dead inside, they're dead. And that'll be our lives.

EP | Viewer Mail #1

LOIS: I think you're gonna love this cake.
STEWIE: (Dressed as a girl) None for me, thanks. It's gonna go straight to my vagina. That's what girls worry about, right? Having big vaginas?

EP | Boys Do Cry

LOIS: Look Meg – A: Ear sex is just unnatural, and B: How do I say this, vaginal intercourse is... it's just tops! It's the bee's knees, Meg. Oh, when you rattle it around just right, oh my God! I mean, you remember when we had that old car with the bad shocks, and I used to take the old dirt road on purpose!

EP | Prick Up Your Ears

LOIS: I'm pretty sure our washing machine is pregnant. I don't even know how that's scientifically possible!

EP | German Guy

LOIS: Oh look, Meg, it's your little baby booties, oh and your little bronzed hat... and your tail.
MEG: My what?
LOIS: Nothing.

EP | Fore, Father

BRIAN: I don't know. I guess taking care of this old woman will be just like babysitting, only with bigger diapers.

EP | Brian Swallows and Peter's Swallows

BRIAN GRIFFIN
WISH IT, WANT IT DO IT.

WORD ON SPOONER STREET

STEWIE: Well, you wanna know what I learned this week? Being a grown-up sucks. Women, Brian, what a royal pain in the ass. It's like, it's like why can't you just hang out with guys, you know, just live with someone of your own sex, just do what you do with women, but with your buddy. You know what, why don't guys just do that?

BRIAN: They do. It's called being gay.

Stewie: Oh, is that what gay is? Oh, yeah. I could totally get into that.

EP | Chick Cancer

STEWIE: Well, all's well that ends well, eh, Brian?

BRIAN: You shot me in both legs and lit me on fire. Piss off.

EP | Patriot Games

CHRIS: Mom, I'm afraid if I fall asleep, the hurricane's gonna sneak up on me and give me a vasectomy.

EP | One If By Clam, Two If By Sea

PETER: Lois, before I found these movies, women only made me cry through my penis. Now they make me cry through my eyes.

EP | Chick Cancer

CHRIS: "You know Anna, when I first saw you, I thought you were the most beautiful girl in the world. And now, all I wanna do is show you my innermost self, but I'm afraid you'll reject me because you won't like what you see. Or, that you'll see my scrotum and see that it has a seam on it and then you'll think I'm made up of two different guys that were sewn together, 'cause that's what I think happened."

EP | Long John Peter

MEG: Chris, get out of here! You're not allowed in my room!

CHRIS: I thought that was just when you were asleep.

EP | The Son Also Draws

SHUT UP MEG

A MARTINI A DAY KEEPS THE FLEAS AWAY

Stewie: You call those cheap implants 'boobs'? They're LIES!

EP | Take Thee, Quagmire

Cool Hand Peter
The boys do prison time!

Cleveland is back for a visit and the boys are in the Drunken Clam having a drink. Their good time is interrupted by Lois, who wants Peter to come home and do chores, which starts the boys talking about how the women in their lives are always trying to get in the way of them having fun. They decide they need a break from their wives and plan to go on a road trip.

Peter declares to the women, "All right, listen up, ladies. We got something to say and we ain't taking 'no' for an answer. We are going on a road trip. We don't know how long we'll be gone, and don't expect a call from us to check in. This trip is about men being men. We will drive after a couple of beers and not make a big federal case about it."

Surprisingly the women are okay with that, feeling it'll give them a chance to have some quality time together. Peter, Joe, Glenn and Quagmire head off to New Orleans together, or the "Home of the All-You-Can-Pee Street," as Cleveland put it. They don't manage to get all the way to Louisiana though, as in Georgia a police car flags them down.

The backwoods policeman immediately decides he doesn't like the Northern city guys (not helped by Peter accidentally making fun of Southern people) and smashes one of the car's lights so that he can book them. Joe tries to appeal to the Sheriff as a fellow officer, but the cop takes Joe's badge and throws it away, before planting a bag of weed in the trunk so that he can send the guys to jail.

Peter, Joe, Glenn and Cleveland end up being sentenced to two weeks in prison on trumped-up charges and are sent to the penitentiary. The guards make sure the new prisoners know they're in for a bad time, and while Peter at first tries to make things fun, he gives up after getting hit in the stomach by one of the guards. The boys are soon put on a work gang, breaking rocks. Peter has an escape plan using a jet pack, but he's forgotten that he's shackled down and so doesn't get very far.

As the days go by, the guys start to realise that maybe they were wrong to have complained about their normal lives and how their women treat then, with Joe

The guards realise what's happening and release the dogs. Peter, Joe, Glenn and Cleveland run faster than they ever have before, trying to outpace the guards and dogs, eventually managing to get away by jumping into the back of a passing truck.

Once they're a bit further from the prison, the boys get out of the truck, keen to find a cabin where they can get new clothes and get their chains off. The house they choose seems like a dream come true, as it even has some handcuff and shackle keys in it. No one seems to think this is suspicious until the Sheriff who arrested them in the first place comes up the drive and they realise it's his house.

The boys hide in the closet, but the Sheriff realises someone is in there. Peter pretends to be the policeman's wife, which initially seems to placate the cop, until he remembers that he doesn't have a wife! The boys make a run for it again with the cop chasing after and shooting at them. Luckily though a train is passing by and the guys manage to jump onboard and head back to Rhode Island.

The quartet of friends think their troubles are over, but the Sheriff has followed them, keen to take them back down South. However they're back in Joe's jurisdiction now and he's called up his fellow cops to protect him. Just as the Sheriff had done down in Georgia, Joe busts the cop's headlight and shoots him in the leg for good measure! Joe tells him, "You took an oath just the same as me, Sheriff. To protect and serve. Not to harass and douche. Just 'cause you have a badge doesn't mean you can treat people any way you like. And as a law enforcement professional, you have an obligation to be more ethically upstanding than the average man, not less. Now, get the hell out of my town."

saying, "Uh, you know something? We left Quahog to find adventure and get away from all those lame chores at home, but I'll tell you this. Looking back on it now, I don't think our lives are so bad."

"Yeah, I sure do miss Lois and the kids," Peter adds.

After two weeks they're glad their time in prison is up, until they discover Southern justice isn't finished with them yet, as the warden tells them another 30 days has been added to their sentence. Another inmate tells them, "That's the way it goes around here. Once you come in, you're never allowed to leave. I got my sentence extended 30 days once. That was 45 years ago."

There's only one thing for it – escape! Joe has a plan, which is to fall out of his wheelchair while they're all out of the prison working, as he knows people always try hard to ignore a disabled person who's struggling so that they don't have to help. While the guards are looking everywhere except at him, the moment Joe is back in his wheelchair the boys make a run for it.

GRUMPY OLD MAN

Retirement is not for everybody

A snowstorm has hit Quahog and everyone's out enjoying the chilly weather. Stewie can't pass all his time in the snow though as he's got to spend the day with his grandparents. The baby's not keen on this as, "I hate being around old people. They've always got weird stuff in their refrigerator."

Carter and Barbara come to pick Stewie up. Once they've driven off, the baby immediately starts to think something is amiss. He's pretty sure Carter has fallen asleep, something that's confirmed when they crash into a tree! Other cars then crash into Carter's, including Consuela, Mayor West and Death, who ends up dying all over again!

In the hospital, Joe comes by to tell Carter they're going to have to revoke his driving license, telling him, "It's obvious your advanced age has impaired your ability to drive safely."

Carter thinks this is ridiculous as he's got all sorts of high-powered business things he needs to do. However Lois and Barbara think it's time Carter starts to take it a bit easier. The old man thinks this is nonsense. "Slow down?! I can't slow down," Carter says. "I'm running a six-billion-dollar company. If I

slow down, the company goes under. Retirement's for old people. I can work till I die. Maybe even after that."

Barbara is adamant though. "But, dear, we are old," she says. "We can't keep pretending that nothing's changed. I mean, we almost injured our grandchild today. Besides, you're always complaining that you don't have enough time to play polo or sit in a chair and moisten your mouth."

Eventually Carter agrees to retire, which has the unexpected side-effect of him wanting to spend a lot more time hanging around the Griffins, just so that he has something to do. Carter tries spending time with the guys at the Drunken Clam, but finds it hard to fit in, especially when Peter starts complaining about Lois. The children and Brian aren't keen on having Carter around more either, as "All he ever does is ask you what you want to do so he can shoot it down and tell you what he wants to do." Even Peter's friends quickly get annoyed with the aging gent, particularly Quagmire, as Carter keeps calling him Quandary.

Lois and Peter are soon at the end of their tether, with Peter keen to get rid of Carter but Lois feeling guilty as he's her father. However they come up with

a solution and present Barbara and Carter with what they think is the answer – a retirement home in Florida. At first Carter is suspicious, but when Peter tells him that in Florida, "Black people's votes go right in the garbage", he's suddenly keen to find out more.

The Pewterschmidts go to visit the retirement facility, checking out the amenities which include a statue of Angela Lansbury – who's apparently a kind of god to old people. There's also a state-of-the-art movie theatre, which includes a button on every seat that will pause the film whenever anyone has a question. Despite all this, Carter doesn't want to move in, saying "There's no way in hell I'm gonna live here! This place is nothing but old people marching to their deaths!"

Peter has a talk with him though, telling him, "Look, Carter, I'll make a deal with you. You give me just one day to show you how great retired life can be for an old fella, and I'll let you honk the car horn one time."

Carter agrees and so the two of them go off to do some old people stuff such as bingo, buying oddly revealing robes and playing with a thermostat. By the end of the day Carter has to admit, "It's not bad at all. Never thought I'd get used to the idea of giving up work and just devoting my life to leisure. I guess this is what people mean by the word 'relax'." Peter and Lois leave her parents at the old folks' home, happy to have gotten rid of them.

Six months later the Griffins get a phone call from Barbara as something is wrong with Carter. Peter and Lois head straight down to Florida and find Carter in a chair, mumbling about cream of wheat, the quiz show Jeopardy and butterscotch pudding. Barbara says she

doesn't know what's happened to him, "He sleeps 18 hours a day, he refuses to bathe, and he's stopped making any sense."

Peter thinks he knows what to do though, taking Carter out of the retirement home and back to the old man's office at Pewterschmidt Industries. At first Carter's senile demeanour doesn't change, but Peter says that the company should start being honest with the IRS and ought to give the employees more rights. This works and Carter rises from his seat, his usual zeal restored now that Peter has given him a reason to live again – ruling his company with an iron fist! He tells his family, "Don't you ever try to stick me in one of those retirement places again! I plan on sitting behind this desk until the day I die. Getting old is right for some people, but not for me."

Barbara, Peter and Lois have to agree, this is probably the best solution.

MEG & QUAGMIRE

Meg turns 18 and Glenn knows she's legal!

The Griffins are at the Teen Choice Awards to celebrate Meg's 18th birthday, even though the newly adult Griffin thinks she might be a bit old for it. She's not as old as aging actor Wilford Brimley though, who is wheeled out to present one of the awards. Wilford can't understand what the hell is going on and decides to put an end to things, pulling out a gun and firing it at a teeny-bopper band who are performing.

The Griffins make it out ok and head home, ready for Meg's surprise party! Sadly for her though, nobody has turned up as no one likes her. Even the $300 Lois gave Chris to try and bribe some of the kids from school to attend didn't work, as Chris had to give the money to Peter to get him to turn up to his own daughter's party!

One person does come knocking though, Quagmire, who knows that Meg has turned 18 and is now an adult. He immediately starts to make his move, telling Meg, "Well, it's your 18th birthday, Meg. That's a very important milestone in a young girl's...I mean, a

young woman's life. Hey, welcome to the adult club, huh? And you know what? You got another member right next door if you ever want to talk and stuff. Happy birthday." He then puts his hand on her leg to see if Meg resists.

Peter says, "Look at Quagmire hitting on that skank. You know he's gonna close the deal." Then Peter realises the 'skank' is his own daughter and is horrified. "Well, gosh, Quagmire," Peter says, "This has been a fun night, but I guess, uh, you better be getting home now, huh?"

Quagmire leaves and Peter vows he will stop Glenn from seducing his daughter, "I tell you something, if he touches my daughter, I'm gonna be kicking butts and taking names! And then giving those names to other people whose butts I kick."

It's not that easy though as Quagmire begins texting Meg, saying what a great time he had and making her feel special. The next day Glenn turns up with a bouquet of flowers for Meg, as the two of them

have arranged to go out together. Peter doesn't want her to go, but Lois unexpectedly doesn't mind, saying, "Peter, nothing's gonna happen. Don't you see? She's only doing this to get a rise out of us. If we fight her on it, she'll only push further."

Peter's not certain though, telling his wife, "Well, she may not plan on sleeping with him, but you don't know how smooth Quagmire is, Lois. He's like a vagician!" Lois seems convinced though.

Quagmire continues his plan to seduce Meg, pretending he's interested in her life and school, and that they have huge amounts of common. However while Glenn tries to convince Meg to come back to his house, she's tells him she'd better not. While Quagmire wishes he could seal the deal, he accepts it'll have to happen another time.

When Glenn enters his house he finds Peter waiting for him, wanting to know if he had sex with Meg. Quagmire says he hasn't, but makes it clear it's only a matter of time. He even asks Peter if he can help him! Peter tells his friend to stay away from Meg, but Glenn doesn't care, "Peter it's me-- Quagmire. This is what I do. Besides, Meg is 18 now and you've gotta let go. You've done your job. It's my turn now."

While Quagmire continues to make his moves on Meg, Peter is just as determined to ruin everything, turning up whenever the two seem to be getting a little too intimate and trying to split the two of them up. Eventually Peter decides to go to Meg directly, trying to explain what Quagmire is like. Meg tells him to stop treating her like a kid and that she knows what she's doing. Lois is still convinced it's all a big game for Meg, but changes her mind when she hears Glenn is taking her daughter to his cabin for the weekend – a

place he only takes women for sex.

The Griffins rush next door to stop Glenn and Meg from leaving, but they're too late as Quagmire revs his engine and heads off. Peter and Lois follow in their own car but get stuck in traffic, allowing Glenn to get the cabin and continue his wooing of Meg. The Griffins don't reach the getaway location until after dark, bursting in just as Quagmire is about to seal the deal. Peter tells his daughter to get in the car. At first Meg gets defensive again, but Peter tells her, "Meg, I'm only going to say this once. You may be an adult, but you're still my daughter, and it's my job to protect you from errant wieners. So, I don't care how old you are, you're going to do what I say and get in the damn car." Meg submits and goes to the car.

Lois isn't about to let Quagmire get off scot free, telling him, "If you ever touch my daughter again, I will cut your thing off and feed it to Brian." They also get him to agree to let them use his cabin once a month. The next day Meg has to admit, she's glad her parents stopped her doing what she was about to do.

The Griffins Through Time

HOW PETER'S RELATIVES HAVE CHANGED THE WORLD!

PETER MAY BE A RELATIVELY NORMAL GUY, BUT HE'S HAD SOME WEIRD AND WONDERFUL RELATIVES, SOME OF WHOM HAVE HELPED SHAPE THE PROGRESS OF MANKIND, WHILE OTHERS ARE JUST DOWNRIGHT PECULIAR.

UR-PETER

Peter's relatives started changing the world early on, as Ur-Peter invented the wheel thousands of years ago in caveman times! As Ur-Brian points out, this is an important achievement, but sadly nobody wants to buy Peter's wheel. Ur-Brian knows that sex sells though, so he gets Ur-Lois to parade around in a bikini. Suddenly all the men want a wheel!

(FEATURED IN: UNTITLED GRIFFIN FAMILY HISTORY)

MOSES GRIFFIN

They don't mention it in the Bible, but Moses was indeed a Griffin who led the Israelites out of Egypt and wandered with them in the wilderness. However Moses Griffin's 10 Commandments are slightly different to the ones handed down to us through history. Rather than worrying about not murdering people and respecting your parents, Peter's ancestor wants, "Commandment #1 – Shut the hell up. Commandment #2 – There's nothing I can do about the sun. Commandment #3 – There are no more Jolly Ranchers, they're all gone. Commandment #4 – When we pass a billboard, please don't read it out loud."

(FEATURED IN: UNTITLED GRIFFIN FAMILY HISTORY)

ANGUS GRIFFIN

The history of sport has much to thank Angus Griffin for, who centuries ago in Scotland helped to invent golf alongside his friends. However even from the very first game, they decide black people and Jews shouldn't be allowed on the course.

(FEATURED IN: BRIAN IN LOVE)

THOMAS GRIFFIN

Peter's great-great-great-great grandfather added to the history of thought, although not much. He was a renowned philosopher, and it seems he mainly thought deeply about being lazy. When we see him, his wife wants him to go out and get a job so the family won't starve, to which he can only answer, "Why?".

(FEATURED IN: PETER GRIFFIN: HUSBAND, FATHER…BROTHER?)

WILLIE 'BLACK EYE' GRIFFIN

Peter's great-grandfather added to the history of cinema as he was a silent movie star, renowned for his slapstick films involving him and a dog that looked like Brian. Each of his short films ended up with Willie getting a black eye and a caption coming up saying, 'Not my eye again!' Sadly for Willie, his fame ended when talkies came, as nobody could understand his incomprehensible voice.

(FEATURED IN: UNTITLED GRIFFIN FAMILY HISTORY)

ULYSSES S. GRIFFIN

While history class tells us the man who helped end the US Civil War was Ulysses S. Grant, he was actually Ulysses S. Griffin, who didn't put an end to the war on the battlefield, but instead settled things by beating the Confederacy's Robert E. Lee in a drinking contest – a much more Griffin way to sort things it.

(FEATURED IN: E. PETERBUS UNUM)

PETER HITLER

History may have ignored Hitler's brother, who is Peter's great uncle, although we have much to thank him for. Peter spent most of the Third Reich being an annoying freeloader and annoying his brother when he was busy doing 'Nazi Stuff'. However he brought an end to his sibling's reign of terror by shooting both Adolf and Eva Braun, and then making it look like a suicide pact.

(FEATURED IN: UNTITLED GRIFFIN FAMILY HISTORY)

NATE GRIFFIN

Peter's great-great-great-great grandfather helped break down the colour barrier at a time when relationships between black and white people were illegal in most of the US. He was a slave, brought from Africa against his will (he was born in Quahogswana), and put to work on the plantation owned by Lois' ancestors. However he ran away with the beautiful Lois Laura Bush Lynne Cheney Pewterschmidt and started a family with her.

GRIFFIN PETERSON

Although Griffin Peterson may not have changed the world, he's very important to the residents of Quahog, as he's the true founder of the town. He was exiled to America by King Stewart after falling in love with the monarch's beloved Lady Redbush. Griffin set up the town declaring, "We're gonna build a new settlement. We'll have a happy new life, and we'll have equal rights for all. Except Blacks, Asians, Hispanics, Jews, gays, women, Muslims, um, everybody who's not a white man. And I mean "white" white, so no Italians, no Polish. Just people from Ireland, England, and Scotland. But from only certain parts of Scotland and Ireland. Just full blooded whites. No, y'know what? Not even whites. Nobody gets any rights. Ahhhh... America."

THE BLIND SIDE

Can Brian make it work with a girl who can't see?

When Peter gets a new colleague who's deaf, Quagmire is excited as he really likes disabled women, feeling "They can do things to you that regular chicks don't even think of."

It sets Glenn thinking, who decides to organise a disabled women's evening at the Drunken Clam, in the hope of meeting some interesting chicks. Seamus turns up to talk to other women with wooden limbs, Quagmire finds a hooker – a woman with hooks for hands who also happens to be a prostitute – while Brian chats up a women at the bar. The dog doesn't realise that Kate is blind until after he's asked her out, but he doesn't seem to mind too much.

A few days later Brian and Kate head off to the cinema for their date. Brian isn't sure it's the best place to take a blind woman, but she assures him "Brian, blind people go to the movies all the time. We just listen. I might be blind, but my brain has been trained to listen to any movie and know exactly what's happening on screen."

Things seem to be going well until they get back to Kate's apartment. Brian tries to encourage her to let him show her to the bed, but she says they'd better wait for a later date to do that. She then hears a dog bark and says, "Ugh! Our stupid neighbour's dog barks 24/7. God, I hate dogs. Yeah, they're just slobbery, annoying, needy little bastards. I'm just not really a dog person, I guess."

Brian isn't sure what to do, as he really likes Kate and she seems to like him, but she hates dogs. He decides that, "I'm just gonna avoid touching her until a little more time has passed. And by the time I tell her, I'll have impressed her so much that the dog thing won't even matter."

Stewie isn't convinced, saying "Yeah, well, good luck with that. You know, I like your delusion, Brian. Most people would say, 'I lost, I give up,' but you, you just keep trying."

Pretending he's not a dog isn't the only lie he tells Kate, as he figures he can use her blindness to make himself seem more impressive than he is. For example he pretends to be a whole pack of muggers so that Kate

believes he fought them off to protect her, and uses a treadmill and a fan to convince her they're in Paris climbing the Eiffel Tower.

By their sixth date Kate is ready to take things further, but while Brian was keen to jump in bed with her when they first met, he's now scared what will happen when she discovers he's a dog. Kate is starting to worry, saying "Brian, this is like our sixth date. I'm beginning to feel like you're not attracted to me or something." Brian insists it's just because he feels strongly about her and wants to take it slow.

Kate then tells him that her parents are coming in to town and she wants them to meet him. At first the dog doesn't know what to do. Kate's parents are sighted and so the moment they see him, they'll tell her that he's a dog.

Brian talks it over with Stewie, who promises to help. A few days later Brian and Stewie arrive at the restaurant with the dog covered head to toe in bandages so Kate's parent can't see him, and Stewie dressed as a female nurse. Stewie explains, "What happened is this one's a hero, is what happened. Rescued two children from a burning building. Can you imagine? Not quite in time--they were both horribly burned. Have that sort of crème brûlée face going on now, but he saved their lives."

Things are slightly fraught through the meal though, such as Kate's mother smelling wet dog when the waiter accidentally spills water on Brian and Kate's father wondering what Stewie is doing there. Things seem to have gone okay though when at the end of the meal Kate's parents propose a toast, deciding Brian is a great guy.

Their praise starts Brian's tail wagging, so Stewie chops it off before Kate's parents see it. Stewie's got rather too into his role as a nurse and decides to

cauterise the wound, causing Brian even more pain. When Stewie attempts to inject Brian with morphine they start talking about the vet, which makes Kate realise there's a dog in the room. Brian decides to come clean, "Yes! Okay? There's a dog in here. I'm a dog! I'm so sorry, Kate. I know you hate dogs, and I...I wanted to tell you--I really did--but I just thought...I thought, if we got to know each other better first, you would eventually be able to see past it."

Kate tells him, "You know what, Brian? I could have gotten over the fact that you're a dog, because I really do care about you and I feel like we had a connection, but I can't get over the fact that you lied to me. You screwed up, Brian. And now you're going to have to watch me walk out that door."

Brian is devastated that he screwed things up so badly, but Stewie has an idea, saying "Well, since Kate is blind, you could probably just do a different voice and go out with her all over again!"

LIVIN' ON A PRAYER
The Griffins turn to kidnapping!

At a children's sing-along at the local library, Stewie makes a new friend called Scotty. Lois and Scotty's mom, Hope, realise how well their kids are getting along and decide to set up a playdate for the two of them.

A few days later Scotty is at the Griffins' house playing Transformers with Stewie. Brian tries to join in but Stewie is trying to be too cool for school and belittles the dog's attempts to merge the world of He-Man with the Autobots and Decepticons. However the attempts at play come to a crashing halt when Scotty collapses on the floor.

Lois is frantic and rushes Scotty to the hospital. Dr Elmer has bad news, Scotty has cancer, although it's treatable with chemotherapy and radiation. When Hope arrives, Lois prepares to tell her the bad news but it turns out she and her husband Ben already know. In fact they're almost annoyed Lois has taken their son to the hospital, saying "We're Christian Scientists. We don't accept medical care for ourselves, and we don't permit it for our children."

Lois thinks this is crazy, but Scotty's parents are certain that "We will heal him with the power of prayer."

After discovering the doctor can't force Scotty's parents to treat him, Lois decides she has to do something and so gets Peter and Stewie to accompany her to Scotty's house, hoping to talk them around. She tells Hope and Ben, "Look, I don't mean to question your religious beliefs, but as a mother, I just can't bear the thought of little Scotty not getting the help he needs."

Hope and Ben are convinced that all they need is God and the teachings of a book called, 'Science and Health with Keys to the Scriptures' by Mary Baker Eddy, which was written in 1867 and sets out the beliefs of Christian Science, telling believers that they don't need doctors (because illness isn't real) and you can pray ill health away. Hope and Ben are steadfast in their belief, saying "Look, we appreciate your concern, Lois, but Scotty is our son and we have to tend to him as we see fit."

Lois implores, "Your son is sick! He needs help!" but it makes no difference. Their beliefs seem crazy to the Griffins but there's no shaking them.

Lois asks Joe if there's anything they can do from a legal standpoint, but he tells her, "There are no laws that say those people have to take their child to the doctor... It's a tricky area, Lois. You could file a suit, but that could take months, and even then, there's no guarantee the court wouldn't support the parents' right to practice their religion."

After talking it over with Peter, Lois decides there's only one option – kidnap Scotty and take him to the hospital. That night Peter and Lois head off to Scotty's house, with Peter keen to get involved in every heist movie cliché imaginable, from being an Asian contortionist in a box to distracting the guards by dressing sexy. Eventually Peter gets into the house, and while he initially kidnaps the wrong child, they eventually get away with Scotty.

News of the kidnapping spreads quickly. Before Lois reaches the hospital, the police are waiting for her to arrive. Joe calls out to them, "Lois, Peter, stop right there. You're under arrest for kidnapping. I'm gonna have to ask you to hand over the baby and surrender."

Lois isn't about to give up though, saying she'll gladly go to prison forever as long as the doctors save Scotty's life. Hope and Ben demand their son back, saying they've "Entrusted our son into the Lord's hands."

"Ben, Hope, I know you don't believe in modern medicine," says Lois, "But you do believe in the power of prayer. And through the years, when there was disease or infection, people of good faith would pray to God for a cure. Well, then isn't it possible that penicillin, vaccines and antibiotics are all actually answered prayers? And isn't it possible that the amazing men and women of medicine who brought about these miracles could be the instruments of God's answers to our prayers?"

Lois realises her words are starting to have an effect, driving the point home by saying, "I mean, what's the point in praying to God if you're just going to wipe your butt with his answers?"

Ben and Hope realise Lois is right and agree to allow Scotty to have the treatment, realising that perhaps modern medicine is God's will after all. The little boy then goes into the hospital, gets his treatment and a few days later Lois hears he's well on the way to recovery. Stewie doesn't care though as he's found a friend he thinks is even cooler, a child with leprosy!

TOM TUCKER
THE MAN & HIS DREAM
Peter Griffin goes Hollywood!

News anchor Tom Tucker isn't enjoying his job, having to do things like being around sick children he's worried might make him ill. His co-anchor Joyce Kinney mentions that Tom used to be an actor, working under the name George P. Wilbur.

Peter is thrilled to hear this, as "That's the guy who played Michael Myers in Halloween 4, the greatest movie of all time. I've only seen that movie about a thousand times. How could I not have noticed that?" There's more exciting news in the Griffin house as Chris has met a girl called Lindsey, who's "Really nice and super pretty, and her bicycle seat smells like strawberries." All he needs to do now is ask her out.

Peter heads down to Channel 5 to tell Tom Tucker how much he loves Halloween 4 and that, "I think that was the most brilliant performance ever in the history of everything, and I wanted to see if you would sign my DVD."

Peter's curious about why Tom didn't make any more movies, with the news man saying. "Well, I tried to make a career out there in Hollywood, but I just didn't realize how tough acting is." After Halloween 4 he only managed to get bit parts, before giving up, moving back to his hometown of Quahog, and winding up working as a news anchor. Peter thinks Tom gave up too easily and vows to help him become a star. They agree to head back to Tinsel Town with Peter as Tom's agent!

Chris meanwhile has plucked up the courage to ask Lindsey out and she said yes! The moment Lois meets her she decides she's an absolutely delightful girl, but Brian and Stewie can't help but notice Chris' new girlfriend looks almost exactly like Lois. "Looks like somebody's getting a little Oedipus-y," says Stewie.

In LA, things don't start out that well as Peter thinks the airport is Hollywood, but it doesn't take him too long to get Tom a small part in NCIS. Tom thinks that maybe abandoning his life in Quahog wasn't so crazy after all and perhaps Peter will make a good agent.

In Rhode Island Lois still thinks Lindsey is a great catch. Brian decides to point out, "Lois, don't you think maybe part of the reason you like Lindsey could be because she looks so much like you?" Lois can't see it, but Brian insists, "Come on, she's clearly an awful person. And I think it's possible that your vanity has made you a little blind to that." It makes no difference as Lois still thinks Lindsey is wonderful.

Peter has a shock when James Woods walks into his office, wanting him to be his agent. It's particularly surprising as the last time Peter saw James, he'd been stabbed to death by Tom's murderous co-anchor, Diane Simmons. James explains that, "Well, gentlemen, sometimes being a big Hollywood star has its advantages... Being a famous movie star entitled me to top-notch medical care not available to the rest of society. My body was immediately taken to a Hollywood hospital where I was hooked up to a 17-year-old ingénue. And in accordance with Hollywood law, her life force was infused into me, bringing me back from the dead."

Now he wants Peter as his agent as Griffin is an up and comer who's hungry for success. It's not long before the excitement of being James Woods' agent leads Peter to dump the "hillbilly from Rhode Island" who Peter originally went to Hollywood to help. Tom is upset but Peter doesn't care as he reckons he's a big-shot now! James turns out to be a lot to handle though, such as demanding he gets to use Peter's apartment at 2.00am in the morning so he can sleep with his cousin.

While out having a coffee with Bonnie, Lois sees Lindsey kissing another guy. When she tells Chris she's surprised that he takes the news well as he knows she's a bit of a slut. Lois can't understand why Chris would date a girl like that, but he explains, "I thought she'd be like you. Well, you got to admit, Mom, she does look a lot like you. I mean, I just look at you and Dad, you know? He's a complete train wreck, and you put up with him. And I'm no prize myself. So, I guess I figured if I don't find a girl just like you, I might never find anyone."

Lois consoles her son, telling him, "Of course you'll find someone. And you are a prize. You're a handsome, kind-hearted, young man, and any girl would be lucky to have you in her life."

Peter's life with James is getting out of hand, and after Peter tries to convince James he needs to play a hayride driver (as he reckons hay will be the next big thing in Hollywood), Woods fires him. Peter goes to find Tom to apologise, admitting he's been a real jerk. Tom forgives him, saying, "Well, I suppose your only crime is that you believed in me. And then stopped believing in me rather abruptly."

The two head back to Quahog, with Tom getting his old job at the news desk back and Peter returning to his home on Spooner Street.

TEST YOUR

DO YOU KNOW EVERYTHING THERE IS TO KNOW ABOUT THE GRIFFINS AND THEIR FRIENDS?

HOW BIG A FAN OF FAMILY GUY ARE YOU? HAVE YOU SEEN EVERY EPISODE SO OFTEN YOU CAN MOUTH ALONG TO THE WORDS? WELL, HERE'S WHERE YOU CAN TEST YOUR KNOWLEDGE WITH OUR FIENDISH QUIZ THAT COVERS ALL 10 SEASONS OF THE ADVENTURES OF PETER AND CO. SEE HOW MANY YOU CAN GET RIGHT!

Permission to FREAK OUT?

1. What is the name of Herbert's dog?_____
2. Who donates a kidney to Peter in order to save his life in the episode 'New Kidney in Town'? (Clue: Brian offers, but it's not his kidney they eventually use)_____
3. What is the name of Quagmire's dad, following her sex change operation?_____
4. In the episode 'The Juice Is Loose', which famed former murder suspect does Peter befriend?____
5. What it the name of Joe and Bonnie's son, who was believed killed in Iraq, until he turns up in the Season 10 episode 'Thanksgiving'?_____
6. Which top Hollywood star seems to have a crush on Peter in the Season 10 episode, 'Stewie Goes For A Drive'?_____
7. In the episode 'Mother Tucker', Stewie and Brian had a radio show. What was it called?_____
8. While Peter was brought up by Francis Griffin, he learns his biological father was an Irishman. What was his name?_____

9. In Season 1, both Peter and Lois ran for the local school board elections. Which of them wins?
_____
10. The loser of the school governor contest was elected to which civic position in the episode 'It Takes a Village Idiot, and I Married One'?_____
11. What's the name of Lois' aunt, who leaves the Griffins her mansion when she dies, in the episode 'Peter Peter Caviar Eater'?_____
12. In 'Chitty Chitty Death Bang' Meg makes a friend who turns out to be a member of a suicide cult. What was the name of that friend?_____
13. Which former US president does Lois sleep with in 'Bill & Peter's Bogus Journey'?_____
14. In 'Patriot Games', which terrible London-based American Football team does Peter get sold to?
_____

15. According to the episode 'Stuck Together, Torn Apart', Mort and Muriel Goldman's niece is which American actress?_____

16. Brian falls in love with an elderly shut-in in the episode 'Brian Wallows and Peter's Swallows'. What is her name?_____

17. What happened to Brian's mother after she died?_____

18. The Griffin house becomes an independent nation in 'E. Peterbus Unum', but what does Peter call his new country?_____

19. What ends Brian's law-enforcement career as a drug sniffer dog in 'The Thin White Line'?_____

20. What is the name of the cigarette company that buys the toy factory where Peter works in the early seasons of Family Guy?_____

21. After the toy factory is bulldozed, Peter buys a boat so he can do which job?_____

22. He eventually ends up working in the shipping department of which brewery?_____

23. In the episode 'Blind Ambition', Peter goes blind while attempting to break which world record?_____

24. Peter's other maladies include having a stroke, but what caused him to have it?_____

25. Chris gets a talking pimple in the episode 'Brian The Bachelor', what's it called?_____

26. Why does Chris join the Peace Corp and run away to South America in the episode 'Jungle Love'?_____

27. What secret do Stewie and Brian discover about Hannah Montana/Miley Cyrus in 'Hannah Banana'?_____

28. What legendary figure does Peter discover working in Quahog's Dead Formats Records store?_____

29. Chris gets expelled from James Woods High in 'No Chris Left Behind', but which incredibly posh school does his grandfather help him get into?_____

30. What operation allows Joe to walk again, in the episode 'Believe It or Not, Joe's Walking on Air'?_____

31. In 'I Take Thee, Quagmire', what is the name of the woman Glenn marries?_____

32. And what's the name of Quagmire's daughter, who's left on his doorstep in 'Quagmire's Baby'?_____

33. One more Quagmire question. What's Glenn's day job?_____

34. What is PTV?

35. Lois was brought up a protestant, but her mother was actually born into which faith?_____

36. What does Peter confess about his children moments before he thinks the world will end, in the episode 'April In Quahog'?_____

37. In 'Road To Germany', Brian and Stewie have to rescue who from Nazi-era Poland?_____

38. What causes Peter to become temporarily gay in the episode 'Family Gay'?_____

39. The episode 'Three Kings' is made up of parodies of stories by which author?_____

40. What is the title of the very first episode of Family Guy?_____

Turn to page 77 for the answers.

MILE HIGH CLUB ★ LONG-STANDING MEMBER ★

BE CAREFUL WHAT YOU FISH FOR

Having a dolphin come live with you sounds fun, right?

Peter is excited when he hears a container ship full of Mercedes cars has sunk just off the coast of Rhode Island. "Holy crap! Did you hear that, Lois?" He says, "All them fancy cars out there in the ocean, just free for the taking? I'm gonna get me a Mercedes!"

Stewie meanwhile isn't having as good a time, as his pre-school is terrible and dangerous for the kids. He tells Brian all about how one child spent the entire day in a drawer and asks, "Is it normal that Miss Emily tied us all to the sink while she went out to return a birthday present?"

Peter, Joe & Quagmire head out to sea with a net and a plan to fish a Mercedes out of the ocean. They don't get a car but they do manage to catch a dolphin, and not only that, it's a talking dolphin (with a British accent) called Billy Finn. Billy agrees to help Peter and his friends get one of the cars, but they turn out to be too heavy, so Billy can only bring up a hood ornament. Peter seems more than happy with this, seeing a hood ornament as being just about as good as having the

entire car. He's so happy he tells Billy, "Hey, you know, if there's ever anything I could do for you…"

The next day Brian decides to go into Stewie's day-care to see for himself how bad it is. When he gets there a group of kids are at a table betting, another is playing with a knife, while another is pooing into the box of crayons. Brian is absolutely horrified, but suddenly changes his mind when he sees the beautiful day-care supervisor, Miss Emily, sunbathing in the back garden. Now he's more interested in dating her than ensuring the kids are safe.

Peter is a little obsessed with his hood ornament, even giving it its own pillow. It means that when Billy turns up as his door, keen to make a go of it on land, Peter feels obliged to help, especially as he told Billy, "If there's ever anything I could do for you…" However it quickly becomes apparent that being in Billy's company for too long might get annoying, especially when he tries to impress Peter with some terrible fish puns. The fat man seems to think having a dolphin in

the house will be fun, but Lois isn't so sure.

Over at the day-care, Brian turns up once again, ignoring the terrible neglect of the children and instead just looking for Miss Emily. Stewie is disgusted with the way he's ignoring the danger the youngsters are in just for the chance to date Miss Emily, but the dog won't be put off, inviting the day-care supervisor out for lunch.

Things at the Griffin house are getting a little fraught, with Billy insisting they watch a documentary about dolphin slaughter and laughing at Peter's fatness when he sees him naked. Peter decides, "I tell ya, he was fun at first, but now I'm not sure I can take much more of him living here." Lois decides that maybe it's time to ask the dolphin to leave, however that's forestalled when Billy gives Peter a sob story about having been thrown out by his wife and also promises him another hood ornament.

Brian is surprised to see Stewie at home when he's meant to be at day-care. The baby says he's escaped because, "I finally stood up for all of us and told Miss Emily we should be given a proper lunch and not just what's left over from her Baja Fresh. And she said I shouldn't raise my voice and pulled me really hard into the other room, and my arm came out of its socket."

The dog is still too enamoured with Miss Emily to raise the alarm, and says that they should just deal with Stewie's dislocated shoulder themselves. Poor Stewie is forced to go back to day-care the following day and is there when Brian turns up for his date. At that

point Miss Emily's boyfriend comes out of the shower. Realising the woman he's besotted with is already taken; Brian suddenly comes to his senses and phones the police about the terrible condition she's been keeping the kids in. Miss Emily is hauled off to jail.

Joe, Quagmire and Peter are all fed up with Billy and so agree to help get rid of him by getting him back together with his wife. While Billy doesn't think his spouse will take him back, the boys are determined. Peter and Billy head back to the ocean and meet up with the dolphin's wife, Joanne. She doesn't seem interested, but Billy tries a simple declaration of love, "Joanne, I am so sorry. I promise I'll do better. You know what? I had to live on the land to learn there might be a million fish in the sea, but there's only one you." She relents and agrees to have him back.

BURNING DOWN THE BAYIT

Peter Griffin tries arson!

Brian is in the garden looking for a bone that he's lost. He sees it just as Peter is about to run over it with his new ride-on lawnmower. It's too late to do anything though, as Peter hits the bone, causing it to fly off the lawn and embed itself in Quagmire's head! Glenn is gushing blood and so the Griffins quickly rush him to the hospital, where Dr. Hartman stitches him up and gives him a prescription for antibiotics.

Peter and Quagmire head over to Mort Goldman's Pharmacy to get the prescription filled. Mort's not happy though, telling the boys, "The pharmacy's going under. I can barely pay my bills." Glenn and Peter are surprised, assuming Mort made loads of money, however he says, "I used to, but it's all gone downhill since Muriel died. She could get away with overcharging people, because they were always mentally undressing her and then re-dressing her once they saw the horrible mess underneath. But in that interval, she robbed them blind."

Peter thinks there's some way they must be able to help out and spread the word about Mort's business.

He and Quagmire think they've got the perfect idea with a 'Buy One Get One Free' offer, but Mort simply can't understand the idea of 'getting one free'.

Their next plan involves advertising the pharmacy by dragging a banner behind an airplane, however when the boys decide to check out a woman undressing in a tall building, things go horribly wrong. The banner snags on an antenna, detaches and falls on a school bus, which then crashes off a bridge and falls into a river, killing everyone on board! Mort is horrified, "Oh, God, I'm ruined! Nobody's ever gonna shop in my pharmacy again! I'm gonna lose everything!"

Mort says he wishes he was as lucky as his cousin, whose business burned to the ground and he got loads of insurance money. The boys decide do the same and set fire to the pharmacy, as while it's a major crime, they decide that the insurance companies deserve it. It turns out Mort is oddly well versed in making arson look like an electrical fault. Quagmire asks him how he knows all this stuff, with the very Jewish Mort saying,

The Drunken Clam

"Oh, it's all covered in the Torah. Right after the chapter on writing complaint letters that will result in compensatory merchandise."

The plan works and Goldman's Pharmacy burns to the ground, with the investigators deciding it must be due to faulty wiring, guaranteeing an insurance payout. It seems they've got away with it, until Joe turns up, saying "Well, you're my friend, Mort. I want you to know that I'm going to personally go over all the evidence. I'd hate to think there's someone in town who's out to get you."

Peter, Mort and Glenn try to convince Joe that his involvement isn't necessary, but he's determined and sets off to investigate the fire. Understandably the arsonists are really worried, with Quagmire in particular seeming upset and saying, "Why did I ever agree to do this? This isn't who I am. I looked in the mirror this morning, and it was like I was looking at a man I'd never seen before."

Realising they're in trouble, Peter comes up with a plan to try and stop Joe, phoning him up, pretending to be the chief of police and firing him. However he reinstates him once Joe says he was gonna give the chief a birthday present, and so instead of getting Joe off the case, Peter spends the next week trying to become police chief in order to get the pressie!

Next they try to distract Joe by sending him annoying text messages about what he wants for dinner to try and get him to make mistakes in his investigation and miss seeing any evidence against them. They then pocket dial Joe to really annoy him. It turns out this was a bad idea though, as it causes Joe to discover this isn't the only time Peter's pocket dialled him. The last time was on the night of the fire, during which Peter confessed, "Oh, my God, look at that fire we started, Quagmire and Mort. You know who

I don't miss is Joe."

Joe confronts his friends with this evidence and arrests them. He takes Mort, Peter and Quagmire down to the police station and begins to interrogate them. The boys' alibi soon begins to crack and while Joe says he doesn't want to charge them, they committed a crime and he doesn't have a choice. Lois meanwhile is horrified about what Peter has done, telling him "Peter, how could you do this? You have a family. Did you ever stop to think about us before you did something that could send you away to prison?" To which he replies, "For once, could you visit me in jail and not criticise me?"

Eventually though, Peter manages to convince Joe that insurance companies are bad, reminding him how they refused to pay for a treatment that would have allowed him to walk again after the accident that left him in a wheelchair. Joe agrees to lose the evidence that would have seen his mates rotting in jail and lets them go free.

KILLER QUEEN

Return of the Fat guy Strangler?

Peter is excited when he hears that hot dog eating champion Charles Yamamoto is heading to Quahog for a contest. Chris says his dad should enter the competition, but Peter replies, "Well, I would, Chris, if I wasn't so obsessed with my figure. Wait a minute. Chris, have you ever eaten anything?" And so a plan is born to enter Chris into the competition. But first they need to find the $50 to enter.

Peter decides to sell some of his stuff, which causes Brian to find a copy the Queen album, 'News Of The World', which absolutely terrifies Stewie when he sees the cover art of a scary looking robot holding bloodied humans in its hand. Seeing the baby's reaction, Brian realises he could have some fun, with the dog agreeing to give Peter the $50 dollar entry fee in return for the album. For the next few days Stewie can barely do anything without the scary robot picture showing up and making him jump.

After training, Peter & Chris head for the competition determined to take down Charles Yamamoto. When the contest starts, Chris seem to be doing well, but he soon start to wane and near the end he's four hot dogs behind the champion. Thanks to a last minute rally, Chris shoves more food down his throat and wins.

While he may be a winner, Lois is not happy, as not only did she tell Peter not to enter their son in the contest, but "Chris is already overweight. We need to start taking responsibility for his health. So I decided to sign him up for fat camp." Chris doesn't want to go, but Lois is determined.

When they show up at the 'Fresh Start Teen Weight Loss Camp', Chris points out this it's unfair he has to go to fat camp when his father is bigger than he is, and so Peter gets signed up too. Peter thinks he'll be okay at fat camp, trying to be the 'cabin clown' and telling the boys scary stories about being made to eat salad.

Brian meanwhile is still scaring Stewie with the Queen album cover, to the point where the baby is so terrified he makes a suicide pact with his teddy bear so they can go out on their own terms rather than being eaten by the scary robot. Brian realises things have gone too far, telling him, "Look, Stewie, I'm sorry for scaring you, all right? But come on, it's not a real robot. See? It's just an album. Look. Here, you want to hit it?" While Stewie isn't certain, he comes to realise it's just a picture and decides to forgive Brian.

Back at fat camp things take a rather disturbing turn. One of the campers has been killed! Peter can't help but notice that a fat kid getting strangled is suspiciously like the MO of Lois' psychotic brother Patrick, who's better known as 'The Fat Guy Strangler'. However Patrick is locked up in an insane asylum – at least that's what they think until there's a knock on the Griffin house door, and there stands Patrick.

Lois takes him to the fat camp, feeling her brother must have something to do with the murder. After all, it's a big coincidence Patrick got out on the same day a fat kid was strangled. Joe plans to arrest Patrick, telling him, "We know you escaped from the asylum and killed...Bill, we'll just call him "Bill" for now."

"Escaped? I-I didn't escape," says Patrick, "Just this morning, a very nice gentleman opened my cell door and said I was free to go." Joe's not convinced.

However it turns out Patrick probably wasn't the killer when another boy is strangled while Patrick is at the Griffins' house with Joe and Lois. Indeed, it's lucky Patrick is there, as he can use his inside knowledge of being a homicidal killer to tell the police what's likely to happen next, saying "He's 'feeding.' He killed twice and he's gonna do it again. He's got plenty of places to hide out there and a fully stocked corral of victims."

Looking into the killing, Patrick has a revelation, realising the murderer isn't strangling just any fat person, he's actually after Chris but keeps getting the wrong person. But who would want to kill the teenager? Realising the danger, the Griffins decide to give up on fat camp and head for the safety of home.

That evening Chris is getting ready for bed when Charles Yamamoto appears and says, "You dishonoured me, Chris Griffin. No one has ever eaten more hot dogs than me. Now you must die!" Charles is the killer! After a brief fight, Chris hits Charles with a rock. However this isn't enough to stop the murderer. Luckily Stewie turns up with the Queen album cover and terrifies Charles with the creepy picture, causing him to drop dead.

Later Patrick sees the dead body and realises Charles was the man who let him out of the asylum. Joe explains, "Well, then it all makes sense. Yamamoto wanted it to look like you broke out on your own. That way, when he murdered Chris, it was a cinch that you would take the blame. Well, Patrick, I guess we all owe you an apology."

Patrick still ought to go back to the asylum though, but in a brief moment when everyone is looking the other way, he escapes off into the night!

THE WORD.

SAY HAVE YOU HEARD?

IF YOU HAVE EAGLE EYES, THEN SEE IF CAN HUNT DOWN THE WORDS IN OUR QUAHOG INSPIRED WORDSEARCH.

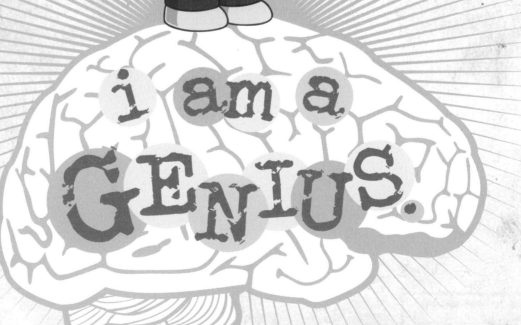

GOOD LUCK.

SEARCH!!!

```
M U R I E L G O L D M A N A N A N F E C I I I N R N I A
L I E E S L C L A K M E C G O H A U Q F I A W R U E
E R A E D I A N E S I M M O N S W E N 5 N O I T C A
P I G R P J N C E N I N E I I I A H D I R I I I E T
S G E Y O A O U R E N T N M F E N P I B E A T D E O
R E N E S S T Y K S R Q E A F N A M D L O G T R O M
H D S K A D R R C A O G G U I I K N M M A R C T M T
O N D N C S U L I E L C H A R I A L T E N W D A L U
D G S O J L B N N C K I E T G L T R B H H I Y O N C
E R J M J I R U L O K I M F E M A E R A M O R I G K
I O E L A G A S E I S P N V I S I L U H R E F N R E
S U S I E S W A N S O N E N W D C R C W T F W E A R
L A I V J A K F A N E L A W E O I S E T I N L H R E
A S T E N N C G L E C E I W T Y R S A R O B X E K E
N L S O I E I E R F I D P D S E T B G O I R A N I O
D S E L B A R B A R A P E W T E R S C H M I D T A E
E I W X R P T S F A I E T W S O I S W A C A R I S J
I E L E B R A R C L W I E T W R T N C O I N R K I S
H M O U E O P W A R I P R N H N A J N H I G C L H F
A E R E O V R L M A R E G C A E S T S O M R L A E A
L A A C S I I S H E B M R E C S O N W L B I I R J S
I R C R R D P R T R E S I Y U G Y L I M A F D R D N
M N S R J E E R E E A C F A C C E V C N L F R T C R
N N W E W N A H S N I F F I R G S I O L M I R M R I
G I A N T C H I C K E N I F F I R G G E M N R C R S
I E R J O E S W A N S O N N G E T T H P G A E S T A
```

ACTION 5 NEWS
BRIAN GRIFFIN
CHRIS GRIFFIN
FAMILY GUY
JILLIAN
LORETTA BROWN
MORT GOLDMAN
PATRICK WARBURTON
RHODE ISLAND
GIANT CHICKEN

ALEX BORSTEIN
BRUCE
CLEVELAND BROWN
GLENN QUAGMIRE
JOE SWANSON
MAYOR WEST
MR WEED
PETER GRIFFIN
SETH GREEN
TOM TUCKER

BARBARA PEWTERSCHMIDT
CAROL WEST
DIANE SIMMONS
HERBERT
JOYCE KINNEY
MEG GRIFFIN
MURIEL GOLDMAN
PROVIDENCE
SETH MACFARLANE
TRICIA TAKANAWA

BONNIE SWANSON
CARTER PEWTERSCMIDT
EVIL MONKEY
JESSE
LOIS GRIFFIN
MILA KUNIS
PATRICK PEWTERSCMIDT
QUAHOG
STEWIE GRIFFIN
SUSIE SWANSON

FORGET ME NOT

Is Peter the destroyer of the world?

Joe, Quagmire, Peter and Brian head off to play laser tag, even though Lois feels Peter ought to stick around for family night. However he sneaks out, keen to show off his almost supernatural laser tag powers, which allow him to run across ceilings and shoot his opponents when they can't even see him. Peter wins, getting a fake newspaper with a headline declaring that, 'Peter Griffin Eliminates Enemies, Destroys World' to commemorate it.

When they get back home, Lois is furious that Peter and Brian sneaked out on family night, sparing some special anger for Brian, saying he and Peter aren't even really friends. Stewie agrees with his mother, saying "You think you're Peter's pal, but you're really not. You're just his dog." Brian doesn't believe this, as he thinks Peter's his true pal, and to prove it he decides to go to the Drunken Clam with his friend.

While Peter, Joe, Brian and Quagmire are driving to the pub, they get into a terrible crash, knocking them all senseless. They wake up the next day in a hospital, but immediately realise something is wrong. There's absolutely nobody else there and they can't remember who they are as they have total amnesia!

The boys head out to try and find some other people and discover that the whole town is deserted.

Wandering through the streets they come across Peter's car crashed into a pole. They realise there might be a clue as to who they are in the car, and so rifle through the glove box, finding a document belonging to a 'Peter Griffin'. After the fattest one amongst them realises his head fits perfectly in the giant dent in the steering wheel, he realises he must be Peter and that means he lives at 31 Spooner Street.

They head off to find Peter's house and get more clues as to who they are. On Spooner Street Brian starts sniffing and realises he poops a lot of one of the lawns, and so decides he must be that person's dog. That lawn happens to be Quagmire's, but as they can't remember that they actually hate one another, Brian decides he must be Glenn's dog.

Joe has also found his house, although he's decided the fact he has a police uniform means he must be a stripper! Hints of the boys' original personalities begin to leak out, with Brian and Glenn beginning to snipe at one another and Quagmire more worried about trying to repopulate the Earth than working out what's actually going on.

While they're all in Peter's house, Joe sees something he thinks is a clue to what happened to the rest of the world's population – the fake newspaper

Peter won at laser tag, which says, 'Peter Griffin Eliminates Enemies, Destroys World'. They decide this means the fat man must be responsible, with Joe saying, "Well, he's clearly not just a guy. He's some kind of omnipotent alien, with powers we can only guess at."

Heading over to Quagmire's house, Glenn, Joe and Brian try to decide what to do, feeling they have to kill Peter before he kills them. While Brian suggests they just flee, Joe says, "Are you kidding me? He'd catch us. If this guy's an alien, I bet he can fly. He can probably hear us right now. He's probably got a laser beam that can shoot us through the walls."

Brian is sent to keep an eye on Peter while Joe and Quagmire find some weapons. Brian doesn't want to go, but when he spends some time with Peter, he starts to like him and suspects that maybe Peter didn't destroy the world – after all, a man who finds the word 'bum' that funny probably isn't interested in world domination. Brian decides to head Joe and Quagmire off, telling them, "You guys, I'm not sure that Peter's the guy we think he is. He seems harmless and actually kinda nice." Joe takes this as evidence Peter is controlling Brian's mind. Brian says he'll go and distract Peter,

but actually warns him of the danger. Peter doesn't understand why Brian is helping when he's Quagmire's dog, but Brian says, "Because...I don't...I don't know why. I can't explain it. I just...I feel like you're my friend. (sighs) You wouldn't understand."

Glenn and Joe burst into the house, ready to kill Peter, and while Brian tries to stop them, they're determined. Joe fires his gun at Peter. Brian jumps in front and takes the bullet for his friend and is instantly killed!

Suddenly Brian wakes up in Stewie's room with electrodes attached to his head. He's utterly confused about what's going on, but Stewie tells him, "Well, Brian, you proved me wrong... You see, Brian, I conducted a little experiment. Remember our little argument about whether you and Peter were actually friends? Well, I wanted to prove to you that I was right, that your friendship was purely a result of circumstance. So I created a scenario in which everyone's memories were erased, to demonstrate that you and Peter would never naturally associate with one another. But I was wrong. It appears you two have a genuine bond after all."

YOU CAN'T DO THAT ON TELEVISION, PETER

All children's TV needs is Peter Griffin

Fed up with Peter's reckless ways, Lois forces her husband to stay home and look after Stewie while she goes out. Peter reluctantly agrees and the two of them settle down to watch Jolly Farm Revue. Peter is initially annoyed about this saying, "Son of a bitch. I got to spend the rest of the day watching stupid kid shows." However it's not long before he's entranced by the adventures of Mother Maggie and Pengrove Pig. Soon Peter declares, "This is the greatest show in the history of television. Mother Maggie, you are a kindred spirit."

At Meg's school, she's doing a particularly good job dissecting a pig, which causes her teacher to suggest she think about becoming a doctor. He sets it up for Meg to shadow Dr. Hartman at the hospital for the day.

Back at the Griffins' house, Peter is still watching Jolly Farm and has got so engrossed he hasn't been paying any attention to Stewie, who's now managed to get a sweet stuck up his nose. Rather than saying sorry, Peter just moans at Lois for nagging him about it. Just then Mother Maggie makes an announcement

on the TV, "I've had such fun playing and learning with you these last few years, but now, just as bees must leave the hive, I must leave Jolly Farm - not that you asked, but to have fertility treatments - so this will be our last episode of Jolly Farm."

Peter is devastated. "This is going to leave a void, and somebody's got to fill it," he says, and he decides he's the one who's got to fill it. Later on, Lois is annoyed when she sees Peter hasn't started dinner like he promised, only to discover it's because he's on TV with his own kid's television show, 'Petey's Funhouse'. Lois is less than impressed, and when Peter gets home tells him, "Peter, you already do nothing around the house and now you're wasting more time with this nonsense." However her hubby once again ignores her, thinking she's just nagging because she enjoys it.

Meg goes off to the hospital to shadow Dr. Hartman for the day, who turns out to be stunningly incompetent, having to consult a chart he carries

around with him so he know where someone's head or shoulder is.

Peter is having fun with his show, even if its educational value is dubious, as he seems to be teaching kids that most of them aren't special and then starts bullying one of the kids. Lois gets increasingly fed up with her husband's antics, telling him, "This is the fourth night in a row you've skipped out on us to work on your show. Once again, I'm gonna be stuck cleaning up the kitchen, helping out with homework, and bathing Stewie."

Lois insists she's only trying to get him to do his fair share, but he says about her nagging, "Well, it's getting on my nerves. Like, right now, you are the most annoying thing in my life." Indeed, Peter's so fed up with it he invents a puppet character on his show called 'Saggy Naggy', which is obviously based on Lois. Saggy Naggy spends all her time trying to stop people having fun and attempting to get everyone to eat their vegetables. And in return for her nagging, the puppet gets a pie in the face.

At the hospital, things are getting slightly out of hand when the useless Dr. Hartman gets a call and runs off, leaving Meg to look after his patients. Despite having no medical experience, Meg can't be any worse than Dr. Hartman. Eventually though a real doctor comes along and throws Meg out, saying she has no business doing medicine without proper training.

While out shopping with Stewie, Lois gets assaulted by little kids who realise that she is Saggy Naggy. "You're mean" says one. "You stink, Saggy Naggy" says another. Then a little boy rushes towards her and shoves a pie in Lois' face. Other kids join in, throwing shoes and golf clubs at her. After being attacked, Lois is furious with her husband, but he still doesn't understand what the problem is. His only response to his wife being attacked because of him is, "Writers

take from their lives. You married a creative type. You knew this was a risk."

Lois insists, "Peter, don't you understand that I'm just looking out for this family? Besides, without my nagging, you'd probably get yourself killed." He's still not interested and she decides she's not going to say anything about any of Peter shenanigans and see how he does without her nagging. It doesn't take long to find out as Peter has decided that, "Tomorrow on Petey's Funhouse, we're doing 'Who's On First'. I'm gonna play Costello, and Abbott is gonna be played by a live puma." Lois initially says nothing about this ridiculous idea, although when she sees it's really going to happen, she rushes to the TV station to stop him.

Lois arrives just in time to see the Puma attack Peter and munch down on his neck. Luckily Meg learned a few things at the hospital, including how to mend Peter's severed jugular. In the hospital Peter realises that, "I acted like a real jerk, and I'm sorry, Lois. I know you just get on my case 'cause you're looking out for me." Sadly for Meg though, while she saved her father's life, everyone still ignores the poor girl and won't even say thank you.

LEGO MY MEG-O
Meg gets sold into sex slavery!

After yet again being picked on in gym class, Meg doesn't think she can stand spending any more time at her high school. Her friend Ruth suggests Meg comes with her for a semester in Paris. Meg and Ruth are excited when they arrive in France, but don't even get out of the airport before they're approached by a strange man who asks if they want to share a cab. The girls agree, but after the taxi drops them off at Ruth's aunt's apartment, the man makes a mysterious phone call, saying "Hey, it's me. I've got some fresh arrivals for you."

Meg and Ruth are thrilled by their new independence, but it doesn't last long. When Meg phones her father to say she's arrived in Paris, some men break into the flat and kidnap Ruth! Meg hides under the bed, but it doesn't work, and while she's still on the phone to her dad the men find her and drag her out. Peter can hear the commotion and starts to panic. He realises one of the kidnappers has picked up the phone, so he tells him, "I don't know who you are. I

don't know what you want. But I have a very particular lack of skills. I will never be able to find you, but what I do have is two dollars and a Casio wristwatch. You can have one of them."

The man's only reply is the mysterious, "Drakkar Noir", which is the name of a perfume.

The Griffins call in the FBI, who tell them that they're not allowed to start looking until Meg's been missing for 96 hours. Brian and Stewie are upstairs listening to Lois' increasingly panicked conversation with the feds. The dog tells the baby, "Stewie, I think there's only one way we're ever gonna see Meg again. You and I have to take matters into our own hands... Look, you're the only one who's got the know-how and the technology to help us track her down."

Stewie agrees and soon has them on a flight to Paris. The baby also brings a recording of the kidnapper's phone call with Peter, and hopes to use the man's voice to track him down. Once in France they decide to try and use internet aerial photos to learn

what happened to the girls. The duo manage to find pics of them meeting the strange man after they got off the plane. With this info they look for the man at the airport and soon find him. When they show him a picture of Meg, he runs away. The dog and baby chase after him, only to see him get run down and killed by a bus. Rifling through the dead man's wallet they find some new clues – business cards.

Heading for the address on the cards, Stewie tells Brian they're going to pretend that, "We're Eastern European cologne salesmen. We ask them what they want, and when they say 'Drakkar Noir' - which they all will - we'll know if we have our man."

After getting into the house, they get all the men to say 'Drakkar Noir' until finally Stewie's voice recognition software makes a match and they know they've got their man. He's not going to be taken easily though and so Stewie pulls out a gun and shoots the other men in the room, before their target grabs a knife and attacks!

The man and baby wrestle on the floor, with Stewie nearly getting his throat slit before he finally gets the upper hand. Stewie demands to know where he's taken Meg. The man replies they keep the girls upstairs. Stewie and Brian sneak upstairs calling out Meg's name. They find some other girls, but no Meg, who was apparently taken away earlier that evening so that she could be auctioned off! Arriving at the mansion where the sex slave auction is taking place, Brian disguises himself as an auctioneer and Stewie a slave girl so they can get in. Their ruse is soon rumbled though and they're manhandled downstairs and handcuffed to some pipes, just missing Meg's auction.

The boys manage to break free and hit their guard over the head with a pipe, before running off to try and find Meg before she's whisked off to a life of slavery. Seeing her being bundled into a car, they chase after it, catching up to her just as she boards a yacht. When they eventually manage to get onboard, Brian and Stewie fight their way along the decks. Meg is in one of the yacht's luxurious bedrooms, where she thinks the old man who bought her is trying to force her to be a sex slave. However he explains, "You misunderstand. I did not buy you to be my slave. I bought you for my son, and not to be his slave, but to be his wife."

When Meg sees the handsome boy and he woos her with protestations about her beauty, she agrees to marry him... just in time for Stewie to burst through the door and shoot him in the head! Just as Meg is about to shout at him for killing her fiancé, Stewie pulls out a device that wipes her memory of the past few days.

Brian and Stewie take Meg back to Quahog. Peter and Lois and happy to see her, although they wish she could remember more about what happened. At least she's safe though.

THE TOP FIVE

OVER THE YEARS FAMILY GUY HAS PROVIDED US WITH HUGE AMOUNTS OF LAUGHS, WITH PETER GRIFFIN AND HIS FRIENDS AND FAMILY GETTING INTO ALL SORTS OF CRAZY ADVENTURES, FROM BEING LOCKED UP IN A SOUTHERN JAIL TO SURVIVING THE END OF CIVILISATION. BUT WHAT ARE THE TOP FIVE FAMILY GUY EPISODES? HERE ARE OUR PICKS.

I NEVER MET THE DEAD MAN SEASON 1 | EP 2

Only the second ever episode of Family Guy sees Meg getting some very bad driving advice from her father, which causes her to fail her driving test. While heading home, Peter gets distracted and crashes into the dish that provides cable TV to the local area, knocking out television for everyone. He promises Meg a new car if she takes the blame, which she accepts, even though it makes her even more unpopular than she already is.

However, with the entire town hating her, Meg finds it difficult to take the pressure, eventually cracking and admitting that it was Peter who crashed into the dish. The townsfolk are ready to lynch Peter for what he did, but Lois manages to talk them down, convincing them that without TV, they've been able to enjoy all sorts of other things instead. They think she's right and so agree to let Peter go. Indeed Peter is so happy without TV that when normal service is

restored, he ignores the television and goes to a Bavarian folk festival with William Shatner (whose car happened to have broken down outside).

Stewie meanwhile has decided that he must destroy the broccoli he hates by controlling the weather. Using the broken satellite dish and one of his toys, Stewie brews up a massive storm. Lightning destroys Stewie's device but the storm rages on. Lois and Meg are out on a driving lesson, but due to the terrible weather she ends up crashing into Peter and William Shatner, who are out enjoying being barefoot in the rain. It leaves Peter in the hospital in a body cast, and while he still says he doesn't need TV, he has nothing else to do but watch it, and soon gets addicted to the idiot box all over again.

TOP QUOTE:

BRIAN: Hey, barkeep, whose leg do you have to hump to get a dry martini around here?

EMISSION IMPOSSIBLE SEASON 3 | EP 11

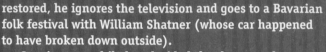

Lois and Peter go to see her pregnant sister Carol. While there Carol goes into labour and so the Griffins get her to hospital. Peter ends up having to deliver the baby himself when Dr. Hartman jabs himself with needles and collapses. This makes Lois broody and keen to have a new baby of her own. Peter isn't sure but soon agrees and the two of them tell Meg, Chris and Stewie they're planning a new addition to the family.

Stewie initially thinks this will be a good idea, but soon changes his mind as he's the baby and doesn't want his position usurped. He vows to do anything he can to stop Lois from conceiving! His initial plan involves smearing lipstick on his father's collar to make his mother jealous and replacing Peter with a robot that insults Lois. However these strategies fail, leaving Stewie no other option than to embark on an even grander scheme – using one of his incredible machines to shrink himself and a spaceship-like vessel down to minuscule size so he can enter Peter's body and destroy all of his sperm.

EPISODES

minuscule size so he can enter Peter's body and destroy all of his sperm.

In his shrunken craft, Stewie makes his way through Peter's insides and is soon at war with the sperm. Stewie has them massively outgunned and manages to destroy them all except one particularly wily sperm called Bertram, who seems to be just as devious and megalomaniacal as Stewie. The two are soon engaged in pitch battle, determined to destroy the other. However as they talk they begin to realise they have a lot in common and that together they could make quite a team. When Bertram reveals that he hates Lois almost as much as Stewie does, the baby decides that rather than destroying Bertram he ought to do everything he can to ensure he is born. After all, together there will be nothing that could possibly stop them killing Lois.

Stewie leaves Bertram and Peter's body, happy that in nine months' time he'll have Bertram as a brother. However while Stewie has been busy inside Peter, Lois has been having second thoughts about having another child, deciding that perhaps she's got enough on her plate. Stewie is horrified, as he's now desperate to have Bertram as his brother. However it seems he's too late as Peter has gone to the bathroom with a lingerie catalogue and may be doing something that ensures Bertram is never born. When Peter emerges, Stewie sees a twinkle in his father's eye, and knows that his sperm-brother is still around after all.

TOP QUOTE:

PETER: It's a beautiful baby girl.
CAROL: Oh! I'm so proud!
PETER: But this girl has a penis.
        Oh, well we'll soon sort that out.
LOIS: Peter, no! It's a boy!

ROAD TO RUPERT SEASON 5 | EP 9

The first of Family Guy's occasional 'Road To...' series starts out with the Griffins having a yard sale. When Brian gets distracted, he accidentally sells Stewie's beloved teddy Rupert. Brian admits his mistake to Stewie, who is horrified and desperate to get his bear back. The baby has soon worked out who bought Rupert, a man called Stanford Cordray. Brian and Stewie head over to his house, hoping to get the bear back, but arriving just in time to see a moving truck heading off to the distance.

A box falls off the back, which says the Cordrays are moving to Aspen, Colorado, and despite Brian's reservations, Stewie's desperation to save Rupert means the dog agrees to go across country to the ski resort to find the teddy. The two hitchhike to Colorado, but have to get over the Rocky Mountains to reach Aspen. They manage to rent a helicopter in return for a grandiose song and dance routine (featuring none other than Gene Kelly), but as neither can fly a chopper, they end up crashing it into a mountain.

Luckily both survive and walk the rest of the way to Aspen, where they find Stanford living in an expensive house. Despite Stewie's imploring, Stanford says he's given the bear to his son and won't let him have Rupert back. Stewie notices that Stanford is a champion skier and challenges him to a race. Brian thinks this is a ridiculous idea, as the baby has no skiing experience. Stewie doesn't think this will be a problem as he has a few tricks up his sleeve.

When they start racing, Stewie unleashes his rocket-propelled skis. Indeed he's so confident in his victory, his skis even build a little house around him with a butler in it, so he can have tea while the race goes on.

This turns out to be a bad idea, as the little house means Stewie can't see where he's going, and so he crashes into a tree, allowing Stanford to win the race.

It looks like Stewie has lost Rupert forever, but he's not a baby to play fair and so instructs the tea room butler to pour hot tea on Stanford's son, which allows him to grab Rupert and run away. He and Brian still needs to get home though, and so Stewie decides to carjack somebody so they can head back to Rhode Island!

TOP QUOTE:

BRIAN: I'm buying you another Rupert. Hey, this one's cute, huh? And if we buy it, they save a real gorilla in the wild...and if we don't, they kill one. Wow, these guys are playing hardball.

PADRE DE FAMILIA SEASON 6 | EP 6

Peter is proud to be an American after he hears Herbert singing 'God Bless The USA' at a Veteran's Day Celebration. He becomes determined to be the most patriotic person he possibly can, showing off his love of the US wherever he goes, and even starts wearing a suit covered in the Stars & Stripes. As a patriotic American, he also thinks it's his duty to make Quahog illegal immigrant-free, even initiating a drive at his work to check all employees are green card carrying Americans.

There's one big problem with this, which Peter discovers when his mother Thelma comes to visit, as she reveals that Peter isn't a US citizen at all. Before he was born, Thelma headed to Mexico to get an abortion, but instead stayed there until she had Peter. She never filled out the paperwork to get him citizenship, and so officially Peter is Mexican rather than American. This means that as a result of his own drive against illegal immigration, Peter is out of a job!

Keen to become a US citizen, Peter take a naturalisation test, but he fails miserably as despite his incredibly patriotic recent past, he knows nothing about his country. His only option is to ask Lois' rich father, Carter, for assistance. Knowing Peter is now an illegal, Carter thinks there's only one thing for it, his son-in-law should become part of the army of undocumented Mexicans who work on his estate. As he's now part of the help, he's not even allowed to stay in Carter's house.

Working alongside the Mexicans, Peter starts to sympathise with the fact that their undocumented status means they get treated badly and receive low wages for gruelling work, when all they want is to give their families a better life. Peter and his family are invited to celebrate Cinco de Mayo with his new colleagues, but Carter breaks up the celebration, wanting them all to get back to work and not caring about them needing a bit of free time. Peter is angry and forms a rebellion.

Realising that this may be trouble, Carter says he'll help his son-in-law get citizenship, but Peter won't back down until Carter promises to help all the Mexicans get their green cards. Carter reluctantly agrees, everyone becomes an American and Peter goes back to his old job.

EPISODES

STEWIE: Are you serious? We come to a mansion and you want to live with the help? Ugh, it's like going to a strip club on a Tuesday afternoon.

GERMAN GUY SEASON 9 | EP 11

Peter decides that Chris needs to get a hobby, but despite trying out several things, Peter can't find anything that Chris likes. However the search for a new pastime leads Chris to befriend an elderly German man called Franz, who owns a puppet shop.

When Herbert sees Chris and Franz together he's horrified. While it initially seems like Herbert's problem is that he's got some competition for

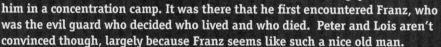

the teens' affections, the old man heads over to tell Lois & Peter the truth, which is that he thinks Franz is a Nazi! The old man tells them about his World War II days, when he was a young Air Force pilot shot down by the Luftwaffe behind enemy lines and captured.

Whilst most captured soldiers were shipped to POW camps, the Germans found pictures of young boys in Herbert's wallet, decided he was gay and threw him in a concentration camp. It was there that he first encountered Franz, who was the evil guard who decided who lived and who died. Peter and Lois aren't convinced though, largely because Franz seems like such a nice old man.

Having failed to convince Peter and Lois, Herbert attempts to get Chris to accept the truth about his new friend, but the teen is having none of it, thinking Herbert just wants to keep him as a source of free labour (Chris remains clueless about Hebert's more pervy intentions). Peter and Chris then go to Franz's house to invite him to dinner, but when Chris is looking for the bathroom, he finds a room full of Nazi paraphernalia. Everything Herbert says was true, but Franz doesn't want his secret to get out, and so locks the Griffin boys in his basement.

Herbert sees Peter and Chris are trapped and goes home, pulls on his old army uniform and heads out to confront Franz. Because both of them are so old, they can barely fight, even needing to stop so they can both take their pills. Eventually though Herbert manages to knock Franz off his front step, and while it's only a short fall, Franz is so old it's enough to kill him. Herbert then rescues Chris and Peter, with the boy realising that despite Herbert being rather too enamoured with him he was his real friend all along.

HERBERT: You know, Chris, all my life, I've wanted to see you locked in a basement. But now that it's happened, all I want to do is get you out!

TEA PETER

Peter Griffin brings the government to it knees

After it burned to the ground, Mort Goldman's pharmacy has been rebuilt and is having its grand re-opening. All the Griffins turn out to wish Mort well, with Peter getting a free 'Come In, We're Open' sign from the pharmacist, which he thinks is cool.

Back at home, Peter is excited to put up his sign, hammering it onto the front door. While Lois tries to explain it's stupid because they're not a business, Peter ignores her. He's hardly put the sign up before a potential customer arrives, sees they're open and asks what they do.

"What do you need?" asks Peter. "Milk," the man replies. Peter realises they have some milk and suddenly the Griffin house is a business! It's not long before others see the sign and flock to the residence. Lois doesn't like having strangers randomly wandering around her house looking at things, but Peter insists, "They're not strangers, Lois; they are our valued customers. And if we don't show them we appreciate their loyalty, they're gonna go someplace else." It's not long though until Joe turns up in his cop uniform

and says, "Peter, I'm afraid I'm here to shut you down. You're running an unlicensed business, and that's against the law."

Peter is furious he can't run a business out of his home and is still railing against it when he meets up with Quagmire at the Drunken Clam, thinking the government should just keep its nose out of his business. He then hears that there's going to be a rally for the Tea Party the next day, which is the group in the US that's angry about government expenditure and its reach into people's lives. At first Peter's unsure, saying, "Tea Party, huh? Well, I'd like to be part of a movement, but what movement would want an angry fat guy with a lot of opinions who hates listening?" But when he sees a firework show that's supposed to show what the Tea Party stands for, he decides this is the group for him!

The next morning Peter announces to his family he's joined the Tea Party. The liberal leaning Brian isn't impressed, saying "Look, the Tea Party isn't the grassroots movement you think it is. It's actually

funded by Big Business types who are using you to get the government out of their way so they can roll over everyone."

When Peter gets to the rally, he's pleased to see so many regular people there who want to stop the government. However when the main speaker gets onto the platform, Peter is too dim to realise it's his filthy rich father-in-law, Carter Pewterschmidt, pretending to be the average 'Joe Workingman'. Carter plays to the crowd, saying the government won't let them do whatever they want to, no matter how dangerous, and the audience laps it up.

Inside the Tea Party headquarters, Peter is surprised but suspicious to see Carter, realising this might be what Brian warned him about. However, Carter convinces him the dog is part of the liberal elite. He gets Peter to agree to be a spokesman for the cause, and puts him in charge of the PR campaign to get rid of Quahog's entire city government.

Back at home, Brian tries to convince Peter that Carter only wants him on his side so he can use him to get rid of the environmental regulations that cost his oil refineries money. Even Lois says that if Carter is involved he's probably using her husband. Peter doesn't listen though, sure Brian is the enemy and Lois is trying to keep him down.

The campaign builds until people are picketing the city hall, demanding the end of city government. Once Mayor West hears so many people agree it's got to go, he agrees that, "Well, I'm nothing if not a public servant, and the public has made its feelings known. I hereby declare Quahog's city government disbanded."

With the government gone, it doesn't take long for things to start to disintegrate, with Peter deciding to drive through people's yards rather than keep to the road, Chris reckoning no one can stop him taking mescaline, and Meg saying that "Now my Spanish

teacher and I can finally hold hands in the halls."

Brian is furious, not just by how quickly order has disintegrated, but that Pewterschmidt Industries is now blasting pollution into the air, with huge clouds of dangerous chemicals hanging over the town. Soon the electricity is down as there's no one to fix it, garbage is piling up in the streets and the toilets don't flush. Peter doesn't know how it could have gone so wrong. "Not having a government worked great in Somalia," he says, "But somehow we seem to have botched it all up."

They decide that as Carter got them into this mess, maybe he can help get them out. However the old man won't even speak to them. Realising that rich people aren't looking out for the little guy, Brian and Peter know they'll have to do it themselves. Peter gives a speech in the town square, where he says that although he's pleased to get rid of the shackles of government, he realises they need a system of rules and someone elected to decide what the right rules are, with all this being paid for with money taken from everyone's wages – he needs a government!

The citizens decide maybe they'll give Peter's crazy idea a try, and soon order is restored.

MR & MRS STEWIE

Finding a soulmate for world domination!

Peter wakes up in bed in the middle of the night and asks Lois whether he can eat a pop tart in bed. However Lois isn't there! At first Peter's unsure what has happened to her, but then he rolls over and realises that she's underneath him and has nearly been crushed to death by his weight. It's so bad she's rushed to the hospital with three crushed ribs.

The next day Stewie is furious at Brian because he made him stay all night at a girl's apartment so that the dog could try to sleep with her. Brian tries to mollify his young friend by taking him to the park. Once there, Stewie meets a fellow toddler called Penelope who's new in town and doesn't have many friends. Stewie seems charmed by his new playmate and is even more impressed when she gets a bully to choke to death on a piece of candy she offers him.

Peter is a bit confused when he finds two single beds in his and Lois' room. Lois explains that it's "Because I'm sick of you crushing me in the middle of the night." Indeed, it's gotten so bad that Lois' spine is now disfigured. Peter can't believe it, as he reckons

he needs someone to cuddle up with in order to sleep.

Stewie and Penelope's relationship moves ahead at full steam, and when he takes a look around her bedroom, Stewie realises he may have found a kindred spirit, as Penelope has an interest in the macabre, does advanced maths and even has a secret room full of dangerous weapons. Indeed, it appears Penelope has gone one better than Stewie and managed to kill her mother rather than just talk about it. "Penelope," Stewie tells her, "I've never said this to anyone before, but I feel like I may have finally found, in you, my one true soulmate." Penelope agrees.

Peter's still having trouble getting to sleep and even goes as far as asking Quagmire whether he can sleep next to him so that they can snuggle. Surprisingly Glenn agrees! Lois thinks it's bizarre her husband wants to have a sleepover with Quagmire. "Fine," she says, "Do what you want. I don't care... but I think it's very strange." The boys go to bed, convincing each other on the way that it isn't strange. They're soon spooning in bed and even go as far as

Quagmire getting naked to make it more comfy!

It's all go for Stewie and Penelope, who are having a riot doing things like trying to plant a wallet bomb on Mort, as well as destroying the Eiffel Tower and Great Wall Of China. It's not long before the authorities are looking for who could be behind the mayhem, but Brian isn't fooled and knows it's the toddlers. When the dog confronts him about it, Stewie doesn't deny it, saying he's always been into world domination. Brian points out that he hasn't been interested in that for a long time. "Stewie, Penelope is taking you down a dark path," Brian says, "Look, in the past you've done terrible things, but it's always been about the pursuit of your greater goal of world domination. But this girl, she just creates chaos for the sake of chaos... She's a bad influence on you, and you should stop spending time with her."

Stewie's not having any of it, convinced they're going to be together forever. However, when Penelope says they should burn her daycare teacher alive, Stewie suggests, "You know, Penelope, maybe we don't have to kill someone every day. There are other things to do." When Stewie says Brian reckons she's a bad influence on him, Penelope is furious and demands that Stewie kill the dog for her!

While Brian prepares to do some writing, Stewie steels himself to commit the murder. Despite bringing out numerous weapons and holding them over his friend, Stewie simply can't bring himself to do it. He goes to see Penelope and admit his failure. At first Penelope seems understanding, but only because she now thinks she'll get to kill Brian herself. Stewie implores her not to, but she decides this means the baby is weak.

Lois goes over to Quagmire's house where Peter has been staying. She admits she's missed cuddling with him too, and that they can get their old double bed back. It's just in time for Quagmire, who's been rolled on by Peter and is now jammed into his spine.

Stewie arrives back home in a panic, warning Brian not to eat or drink anything in case Penelope has booby-trapped it. Not long afterwards Penelope arrives, determined to kill Brian. The dog thinks he can handle a one-year-old, but when she blasts him with a ray gun he has to admit he needs help. Stewie blasts his own ray gun at Penelope, who manages to dodge out of the way. Now it's war, with the toddlers in pitched battle in the street, trying to shoot each other and using all their incredible technology to try to outdo the other. Eventually Stewie manages to overpower her, holding a blade to her throat and screaming, "Stay away from my dog!"

Penelope agrees and kisses Stewie. She then uses a grappling hook to grab onto a truck and is pulled off down the road and out of Stewie's life. Brian asks Stewie is he's alright, to which he simply replies, "I will be. I will be, babe."

INTERNAL AFFAIRS

Joe is a hero but it doesn't mean he's faithful

Joe Swanson is on the news being lauded for leading a drug bust that's taken 100kg of Cocaine off the streets. On the TV he's gives a short speech, saying that, "It feels good to know that, thanks to me and my colleagues, a lot fewer people will be injecting cocaine into their penises tonight."

Later on at the Drunken Clam, all the men there are congratulating Joe on his bust. More than the public attention, the policeman is pleased to be recognised by his boss, and indeed the chief is throwing him a little party later that evening to congratulate him. Peter and Quagmire agree to attend.

When he leaves the bar, Peter gets in his car, pulls out of his parking space and smacks into another vehicle. That would be bad enough, but the car belongs to The Giant Chicken, who Peter has had a long and violent history with. As always when the man meets the bird, they begin to fight. Stewie turns up with his time travel device, which Peter and the chicken end up using to take them to the wild west, where they're trapped between warring cowboys and Indians – but

that doesn't stop them fighting.

Their epic battle continues, returning to the present using a Back To The Future-style Delorean. They then fight their way into a laboratory. Peter and The Giant Chicken end up in a cloning machine, which results in loads of Peters and chickens all fighting one another. One of the chickens is knocked into a machine that causes the whole building to explode, leaving just the original combatants. Not ready to finish fighting, the chicken and Peter next end up on a space shuttle and are blasted into space, crashing into a space station before plummeting back to Earth and hitting an oil drilling platform. While the oil workers flee, the fight goes on until Peter manages to knock the chicken off a tower. The bird gets speared on a pointy branch just as the platform explodes. Peter escapes, but it looks like the end of The Giant Chicken, until he opens a bloodshot eye!

Joe meanwhile is hoping Bonnie will be proud of him, but she seems disinterested and says she doesn't want to go to the party Joe's boss is throwing for him.

The policeman heads off by himself but is upset his wife isn't there to share the moment with him. While feeling low he gets chatting to a policewoman called Nora, who leans in and kisses him.

At the Clam the next day Joe is confused. He asks Peter and Quagmire what he should do about Nora. Quagmire immediately says Joe should sleep with her. The policeman says he couldn't cheat on his wife, but Glenn insists that, "In this case, cheating would be the only fair thing." His reasoning is that the previous year in Paris, Bonnie had an affair with a French man, so Joe would just be balancing things out. Even Peter agrees that sleeping with Nora is the thing to do.

When Joe sees Nora at the police station, she immediately begins to apologise, saying she stepped over the line by kissing him. Joe tries to explain that while he's attracted to her, he can't do anything because he's married. At that moment Bonnie calls but says she only dialled him accidentally. When Joe asks her how she is, she hangs up on him. This is the straw that breaks the camel's back for Joe, who decides he will indeed sleep with Nora.

Soon after it's Joe's son Kevin's birthday, and the Griffins and Quagmire head over to the Swanson house to celebrate. Joe pulls Peter and Glenn to one side and admits he slept with Nora but is now feeling guilty about it. Unfortunately for Joe, they're right next to the baby monitor and Bonnie hears everything! She is furious, and when Joe says she has no right to be angry because she had an affair herself, Bonnie reveals that she never actually had sex with the French man. Soon Joe and Bonnie are having a blazing row, which ends up with both agreeing they want a divorce.

The next day Joe is moving his stuff out of his

house. He reminisces to Peter how sad it is that things have ended so badly, especially when they began so well. Joe talks about how he met Bonnie when she was a stripper. He and his fellow cops raided the club she worked at, but instead of finding criminals, Joe met his future wife. This gives Peter an idea on how to get the Swansons back together. He tells Lois, "Joe just told me how he and Bonnie met. So I figure, all we got to do is find a way to recreate the magic of that night."

Lois agrees and takes Bonnie for lunch at the strip club she used to work at. Peter meanwhile uses a walkie-talkie to call in the cops and get Joe to the club. The policeman arrives just as his and Bonnie's special song begins to play. The husband and wife are surprised to see one another, but Peter's plan works. Joe says to Bonnie, "Listen, Bonnie, I, uh... I just want to say I'm sorry. I was a real ass, and I miss you." Bonnie apologises for being difficult to live with and the two embrace. And just to prove all really is forgiven, Joe gives Bonnie a lapdance.

VIEWER MAIL #2

Three strange tales from Griffin vault

Following on from an episode a decade ago, 'Family Guy Viewer Mail #2' presents three short tales featuring the Griffins. They're based on ideas suggested by the viewers, taking us to weird and wonderful places.

CHAP OF THE MANOR

In the first story, Family Guy is reimagined as a British programme, called 'Chap Of The Manor'. Instead of Peter we have Neville, Lois is Lydia, Chris is Collingsworth, while poor Meg is simply British Meg. As Stewie has a British accent normally, in this alternate Family Guy universe he speaks with a broad Texan accent.

At a pub called the Dog and Cat and Bull and Whistle and Fiddle and Cock and Pig and Wolf and Carriage and Fife and Other Wolf, Neville meets the British versions of Joe and Quagmire. They see a news report announcing that the Queen is due to visit their town the next day. Neville tells the boys that's he's related to the royal family. "Me mum used to claim she was a Windsor," he says. "And to prove it, I'm gonna nick one of the Queen's hairs during her visit tomorrow. And when the DNA proves a match, you'll see I'm royalty."

The next day Neville is out on the streets with his family waiting for the Queen. Brian, who in Britain is a horse, says "My favourite part before the Queen arrives is yelling 'wanker' at Prince Charles as he passes. Wanker!"

Neville meanwhile sets out a mobile hairdressers, running a special offer for queens in the hope he can get her majesty to stop for a trim. It doesn't work and so Neville feels he has no choice but to launch himself at the Queen and try to grab some of her hair. Her driver begins to speed off, but not before Neville gets his prize of some royal locks. However it causes a bit of a disaster as when the Queen heads into a tunnel, followed by a motorcycle, she crashes and dies!

Neville's just pleased he's got the hair, but when he has it tested, he finds out he's not royal at all, and so the Queen died for nothing!

FATMAN & ROBIN

In the second story, Peter is excited because a Comedy Roast is on TV celebrating Robin Williams. However he doesn't understand that at a roast, other comedians insult the person being roasted. "You stop it," he shouts at the TV, "Robin Williams has a manic gift that gladdens a sad world and all he asks in return is our unceasing attention! How can you allow this?! Robin Williams has given us nothing but joy! I wish everyone was Robin Williams!" He's so angry he runs out into the rain and is struck by lightning!

Peter wakes up in a hospital bed and the doctor explains that he's been in a coma. When Peter touches the medic, a strange surge of electricity jumps from his finger and the doctor turns into Robin Williams, complete with the comic's manic energy and vocal riffing. Peter thinks this is great and discovers it wasn't a fluke when he grabs a nurse and she turns into Robin Williams too. Initially Peter vows about his new power, "I will be so responsible with this." This is Peter Griffin though, so of course he isn't! Soon nearly everyone in the hospital is Robin Williams.

Once he's back home, Lois is concerned about how long Peter's new power will last. He doesn't care and hugs Chris and Meg, which turns them into Robin Williams too. Chris starts doing Southern Preacher impressions, while Meg is a sensitive, bearded Robin Williams from the likes of Good Will Hunting. Peter thinks this is great fun and starts turning everyone he meets into Robin Williams. Soon things go a bit far even for Peter, especially when he's in bed with Lois and accidentally turns her into Robin Williams too.

Peter realises his hands have become a curse and he thinks his only way out is to shoot himself! Just as he's about to pull the trigger, the gun turns into Robin Williams. He them tries to throw himself in front of a car, but even that turns into a vehicle shaped like the comic. Eventually Peter has to come to terms with

what's happened, sending all the Robin Williams to spread laughter across the country, while settling down with his now more comedic family.

POINT OF STEWIE

In the final story, everything is seen from Stewie's point of view. When he wakes up, Lois comes to change her baby's diaper. He spews a stream of vitriol at her, but she can't understand.

Later that day he wants some Twinkies, and so uses one of his incredible inventions to get up to the cabinet the treats are hidden in. He grabs a Twinkie and heads outside, ready to stuff the sweet into the exhaust pipe of Brian's car. The baby prepares for his prank, but gets it a bit wrong, as when Brian starts the car, the Twinkie shoots out and hits him in the face. He wipes the cream off, just in time to grab onto the underside of the car and ride underneath it through Quahog. However he's horrified when Brian runs over a squirrel, which gets stuck to the wheel right near Stewie's face.

When Stewie is having a bath that evening, the baby is adamant that he doesn't want his face washed. However he's mesmerised by a frog faced wash cloth, not realising that this is what the dastardly Lois will use to try and clean him. Things get even worse for him when Peter arrives, strips and decides to join Stewie in the tub, much to the baby's horror.

Just before bedtime, Lois comes into to read him a bedtime story; the rather unusual picture book, 'Good Night Town From Footloose'. While Stewie wants his story, Peter has other things on his mind. He says to Lois, "I got a story. It's about the little penis that could. It thinks it can, it thinks... In fact, it's pretty sure it can. It's gonna." Lois tells Peter to go wait for her in the bedroom, while she puts Stewie to bed. Soon Stewie is fast asleep.

GOODBYE FROM

THE LIGHTS ARE GOING DOWN ON ANOTHER YEAR ON SPOONER STREET, WHEN PETER AND CO. HAVE GOTTEN UP TO ANOTHER SERIES OF CRAZY ADVENTURES.

Who would have thought a dolphin would have come to live with the Griffins? Or that Kevin Swanson wasn't dead after all and had just deserted the army? Well, to be honest, if you've been following the Griffins over the years, nothing should surprise you!

You'll be pleased to hear though that this isn't the end. Family Guy will be back with Season 11, and the gang behind the show are already hard at work on the next set of episodes that'll make us laugh and cry. Who knows what they'll be getting up to, but it can't be crazier this Season 10, can it? Knowing Family Guy, it'll definitely try!

But what have we learned from Season 10? Well, we know that the Griffins can make even the Amish violent; Quagmire will try to sleep with Meg (bleugh); and that Mort Goldman is an expert arsonist. Plus Lois' homicidal, fat guy strangling brother Patrick is now out of the insane asylum, so what does that mean for the future (fat people lock your doors)?!

It's goodbye for now from Peter, Lois, Chris, Meg, Stewie, Brian, Joe, Quagmire and the rest of the gang, but it won't be long until they're back, making you laugh once more.

SPOONER STREET

ANSWERS

CROSSWORD

PAGE 24

DOWN

1 Takanawa (6,8)
3 Rhode island (5,6)
4 Patrick Warburton (7,9)
5 Bonnie (6)
7 Peter Griffin (5,7)
9 Seth MacFarlane (4,10)
13 Pewterschmidt (13)
14 Patrick (7)
15 Chris (5)
17 Alex Borstein (4,8)
18 Pawtucket Patriot (9,7)
19 Carter (6)
21 Herbert(7)
23 Megan (5)
27 Jasper (6)
28 Ollie Williams (13)
29 Mort Goldman (4,7)
30 Joe Swanson (3,7)
31 Gilligan (8)
32 Rupert (6)
34 Stewie (6)
35 Francis (7)
36 Jesse (5)

ACROSS

2 Tom Tucker (3,6)
6 Quahog (6)
8 Brian (5)
10 Joyce Kinney (5,6)
11 Bertram (7)
12 Mila Kunis(4,5)
16 Barbara (7)
20 Mexico (6)
22 Susie (5)
23 Mayor West (5,4)
24 Cleveland Brown (9,5)
25 Monkey (6)
26 Consuela (8)
29 Muriel (6)
33 Glenn Quagmire (5,8)
37 Spooner Street (7,6)
38 Thelma (6)
39 Mickey McFinnigan (6,10)
40 Seth Green (4,5)

TEST YOUR KNOWLEDGE

PAGE 48

1. Jesse
2. Dr. Elmer Hartman
3. Ida
4. O.J. Simpson
5. Kevin
6. Ryan Reynolds
7. Dingo and the Baby
8. Mickey McFinnigan
9. Peter
10. Quahog Mayor
11. Marguerite
12. Jennifer
13. Bill Clinton
14. The London Silly-Nannies
15. Jennifer Love-Hewitt
16. Pearl Burton
17. She was stuffed and turned into an end-table.
18. Petoria
19. He gets addicted to cocaine.
20. El Dorado Cigarette Company
21. Fisherman

22. Pawtucket Patriot
23. Most Nickels Eaten
24. Eating 30 hamburgers in a row.
25. Doug
26. To avoid freshman hazing.
27. She's a robot.
28. Jesus
29. Morningwood Academy
30. Leg transplant
31. Joan
32. Ann Lee Quagmire
33. He's an airline pilot
34. A TV channel Peter sets up after normal television gets censored.
35. Judaism
36. He hates being around them.
37. Mort Goldman
38. A medical experiment he takes part in.
39. Stephen King
40. Death Has A Shadow

WORD SEARCH

PAGE 56

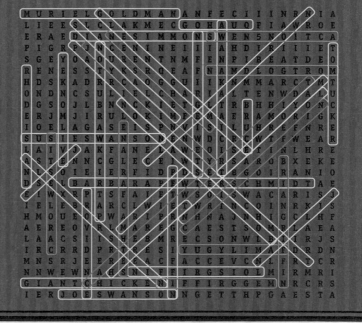

THE QUAHOG INFORMANT